HEINEMANN EDUCATIONAL
A division of Heinemann Educational Books Ltd.,
Halley Court, Jordan Hill, Oxford OX2 8EJ

OXFORD LONDON EDINBURGH
MADRID ATHENS BOLOGNA PARIS
MELBOURNE SYDNEY AUCKLAND SINGAPORE TOKYO
IBADAN NAIROBI HARARE GABORONE
PORTSMOUTH NH (USA)

First published 1993
94 95 96 97 10 9 8 7 6 5 4

A catalogue record for this book is available from the British Library
on request.

ISBN 0 435 80041 8

IN MY MOTHER'S MEMORY

Designed by Mike Brain, Oxford
Typeset by Taurus Graphics, Kidlington, Oxon
Printed by Clays Ltd, St Ives plc

Contents

The Great, the Good and the Holy

Thoughts for a Day

Love Thy Neighbour as Thyself

Acknowledgements

The authors and publishers would like to thank the following for permission to reproduce copyright material on the pages noted:

Action Aid for 'Sobura's Story' by Olivia Bennett published in *Common Cause* (pp270–3); Angel Press, Gooday Publishers for Passage No. 53 from *Give Peace a Chance* by John Ferguson 1988 (pp166–7); Canon Richard Askew and Bath Abbey for an excerpt from a leaflet entitled *Welcome to Bath Abbey* (pp145–6); Batsford for 'The Dreamer and the Treasure' from *Icelandic Folktales and Legends* by Jacqueline Simpson 1972 (pp71–3); Behrman House, Inc. for excerpts from chapter 14 of *When a Jew Celebrates* by Harry Gersh (pp5–7); Rabbi Lionel Blue for 'A Happy New Year' in *Bright Blue* published by BBC Books, © Lionel Blue 1985 (pp2–4); Centrepoint Soho for excerpts from 'One Aspect of Homelessness' and 'On the Streets' from the 1989/90 Annual Report (pp263–6); Chansitor Publications Ltd for excerpts from 'Holi' in the *Living Festivals Series* by Janis Hannaford (pp30–3); Christian Aid for 'When Writing to Your MP is Not a Waste of time' by John Montagu published in *Christian Aid News* No. 55 1987 (pp245–6); The Crown's Patentee, Cambridge University Press for Extracts from the Authorised Version of the Bible (The King James Bible), the rights in which are vested in the Crown (p60); Dell Books, a division of Bantam Doubleday Dell Publishing Group, Inc. for 'Priscilla and the Wimps' by Richard Peck © 1984 from *Sixteen: Short Stories* ed Donald R. Gallo (pp107–10); Direct Results for a leaflet entitled 'Oral Rehydration Therapy: How you can help stop the world's biggest child killer' (pp284–5); Richard Drew Publishing for an excerpt on 'Mary Slessor' from *Scottish Heroes and Heroines of Long Ago* by Eileen Dunlop and Antony Kamm (pp159–61); Evans Brothers Ltd for excerpts from *Edith Cavell* by Nigel Richardson (pp162–5); Evening Standard/Solo for 'Men Swear, Women Cry' by Kate Wharton (pp291–5); Fellowship of Christian Athletes for 'The Long Silence' by A.T.L. Armstrong (pp207–9); Gill and Macmillan, Dublin for 'Lord, I have time' from *Prayers of Life* by Michel Quoist (pp212–14); Mrs Nicolete Gray and The Society of Authors on behalf of the Laurence Binyon Estate for *For the Fallen (September 1916)* by Laurence Binyon (p14); Greenpeace Ltd for an excerpt from a poster entitled 'Against all odds' (pp286–7); Kate Hall for 'Well, Well, Well' by Kate Hall from *A Girl's Best Friend*, ed Christina Dunhill first published by The Women's Press Ltd, 1987, 34 Great Sutton Street, London EC1V 0DX (pp252–4); Harper Collins Publishers Ltd for excerpts from 'Kwuz' from the *The Book of Witnesses* by David Kossoff (pp82–4); for 'Whatsoever You Do' by Mother Teresa from Something *Beautiful for God* by Malcolm Muggeridge 1971 (pp177–8); for excerpts from *The Screwtape Letters* by C.S. Lewis published by Collins Fount, an imprint of Harper Collins Publishers Ltd (pp230–1); Stewart Henderson for 'Splintered Messiah' by Stewart Henderson from *Whose Idea of Fun is a Nightmare?* published by Musical Gospel Outreach (pp205–6); A.L. Hendriks for an excerpt from 'An Old Jamaican Woman Thinks About the Hereafter' from *To speak Simply: Selected Poems* by A.L. Hendriks published by Andre Deutsch (p181); *The Independent* for 'The Typical Teenager is a TV Addict' by Peter Wilby from *The Independent* (pp236–8); John Johnson Ltd, London, on behalf of the author for an excerpt from 'Warning' by Jenny Joseph from *Selected Poems* 1992, © Jenny Joseph (p290); The Khaleej Times for an article on Ramadan (pp57–9); The Leprosy Mission for 'Miti's Story' and 'The Counting Game' by Graham Aylmer published in the Autumn 1988 and the Summer 1989 editions of *New Day* respectively (pp275–7); Lion Publishing plc for excerpts from *The 20th Century Plague* by Caroline Collier (pp255–9); Methuen London for an excerpt from *Bright Morning* by Don Haworth © Don Haworth 1990 (pp104–6); for an excerpt from *The Secret Diary of Adrian Mole Aged 13 ³/₄s* by Sue Townsend (p288); National Curriculum Council for a parable from *Why do Men Suffer?* that formed part of the Schools Council Journeys into Religion project (pp88–9); Thomas Nelson for an excerpt from *Worlds of Difference* by Martin Palmer and Esther Bisset (pp191–3); The Observer for excerpts from 'Tunnel Vision' by Simon Hoggart (pp296–8); Oxford University Press for 'Mothering Sunday' by George Hare Leonard from *The Oxford Book of Carols* (pp28–9); Pavillion Books for 'The Serpent King' from *Seasons of Splendour* by Madhur Jaffrey (pp79–81); Penguin Books Ltd for excerpts from *The Metamorphoses of Ovid* translated by Mary M. Innes and adapted by Guy Williams published by Penguin Classics 1955, © Mary M. Innes 1955 (pp67–8); for 'The Last Flower' from *Vintage Thurber Volume 2* by James Thurber published by Hamish Hamilton 1976 collection © Hamish Hamilton 1963, © Estate of James Thurber 1961 (pp118–20); for excerpts from *The Book of Margery Kempe* translated by B.A. Windeatt published by Penguin Classics 1985 © B.A. Windeatt 1985 (pp155–8); Penguin USA, Inc. for 'The Creation' by James Weldon Johnson from *God's Trombones* 1927 The Viking Press, Inc., © renewed 1955 by Grace Nail Johnson. Used by permission of Viking Penguin, a division of Penguin Books USA Inc. (pp63–6); Laurence Pollinger Ltd and the Estate of Frieda Lawrence Ravagli for 'Beautiful Old Age' by D.H. Lawrence (p289); Random House UK Limited for excerpts from two parables, 'Bahaudin' and 'Abboud of Omdurman' from *Thinkers of the East* by Idries Shah published by Jonathan Cape (p62 and p290 respectively); Routledge for an excerpt from *The Autobiography of Bertrand Russell;* Scholastic Children's Books for excerpts from *Accidents Will Happen* by Andy Tricker 1987 (pp260–2); SCM Press Ltd for excerpts from *A New People's Life of Jesus* by William Barclay 1965 and excerpts from 'Theology and Falsification' by Basil Mitchell in *New Essays in Philosophical Theology* eds Antony Flew and Alasdair MacIntyre 1956 (pp140–4 and pp179–80 respectively); Simon and Schuster Young Books, Hemel Hempstead, UK for excerpt from *Law and Order* by Adam Hopkins and Gaby Macphedran 1985 (pp267–9); The Telegraph plc for three Sunday Telegraph Mini-Sagas from *The Book of Mini Sagas II*, © Alan Sutton Publishing/Sunday Telegraph Ltd 1988 (pp116–17); United Nations for Articles 1–21 of The Universal Declaration of Human Rights (pp242–4); VSO for an excerpt from a leaflet entitled 'This child is about to poison herself' (pp278–80); *The Winchester Churchman* for 'Heaven a Lighthearted Guide for Travellers' (pp232–4).

The publishers have made every attempt to contact the copyright holders. If any material has been incorrectly attributed, the publishers would be pleased to make the necessary arrangements at the earliest opportunity.

Introduction

THE 1944 EDUCATION ACT stated that 'the school day in every school ... shall begin with collective worship on the part of all pupils in attendance at the school' and required that it should be 'a single act of worship attended by all such pupils unless ... the school premises are such as to make it impracticable to assemble them for that purpose'.

By the mid-1980s, the Act had fallen into disrepute and often was not observed – even allowing for the variations permitted by the latter clause quoted above.

But then came the 1988 Education Reform Act, which placed a new emphasis on a daily 'act of collective worship' in schools. It also stressed that this worship should be 'broadly Christian'. 'Hurray!' said the traditionalists. 'It's what we've always been doing,' said some of the church schools.

But the Act has also caused confusion, uncertainty and even anger. How 'broad' is 'broad'? How can you make someone (especially a truculent teenager) 'worship'? Other problems and questions of conscience arise, especially in predominantly multi-cultural schools.

What can be said is that many more assemblies are now being held in schools than there used to be, and that there are many more assembly leaders urgently in need of inspiration – or at least practical help. For it seems that schools *are* observing the new Act rather more closely than they did the 1944 one. This does not, however, mean that the whole school (or even 'years') are coming together for regular daily acts of worship or even assemblies. 'Assembly' may form a part of a class registration period, conducted by a form teacher. Once or twice a week, a whole year may come together for a more conventional assembly; sometimes years may combine – as may houses and other groupings.

Many teachers have taken heart from one reading of the Act which suggests that so long as a majority of assemblies are 'Christian', then the Act is being observed. But teachers are also aware that assemblies (the word is more comfortable to use than the phrase 'act of worship'!) 'must reflect the broad traditions of Christian belief to an extent and in a way which gives them a Christian character'.

It is for all these circumstances that this 'broadly Christian assembly book' has been compiled. Thus it includes passages about the other world faiths, but offers more Christian passages than might have been found in a comparable anthology published ten years ago. This is not a book for those whose creed is 'Just stick to God, most people believe in him – but don't bring his Son into it.'

And it must be remembered that *One Hundred Readings for Assembly* is only a resource, not a course. It is not suggested that any assembly leader work steadily through the collection, day by day or week by week. Nor will every passage be suitable in every context. As the Act reminds us, any materials must be 'appropriate having regard to the family background, ages and aptitudes of the pupils involved'. Nor do I imagine that every user of the book will wish to endorse (and consequently read) every passage it contains. However, I have not included anything I would be embarrassed to stand up and read aloud myself and I hope that whoever uses this anthology will find plenty of passages that engage those who hear them.

I have chosen passages that have an immediate aural appeal and that 'come off the page' easily. (Some I wrote originally for broadcasting: they are 'spoken word scripts' rather than written essays.) I hope I have included pieces that will entertain, stimulate and even provoke. Most, I trust, will be new to even the experienced assembly leader, but I make no apology for including one or two old favourites to which I have found myself returning. The aim of this book is to be convenient as much as novel!

I have resisted any temptation to label individual passages as being particularly suitable for given age groups. That would, I feel, merely patronise the user of the book. He or she is the best judge of the 'sophistication' or maturity of those to whom he or she will be reading. And, after all, what works well one year with, say, Year 9 may seem inappropriate for their successors twelve months later or for their contemporaries in another school.

But the hundred passages have been arranged in five sections. The first twenty seasonal readings ('Festivals of Faith') are arranged chronologically through a year and the majority (but not all) are probably more suited to the younger end of the secondary age range. A calendar (page 299) includes other dates for the seasonal use of material in this book.

The readings in the second section ('Stories, Parables and Legends') all have a strong narrative thread and again are aimed at younger pupils. The twenty readings about 'good people' in the third section ('The Great, the Good and the Holy') are presented in historical order and should appeal to a wide age range. The fourth section ('Thoughts for a Day') is more overtly religious and will, it is hoped, encourage experiential exploration of religious ideas as well as explaining the beliefs of others.

The final section ('Love Thy Neighbour as Thyself') is more concerned with social issues. Here there is a thematic sequence leading from 'the pupil and where he or she is now' to the ultimate. This section could, in fact, be used as a course of readings. The last two sections both include passages that are especially suitable for older pupils and include some readings that will be useful to those who, since the 1988 Act, have been surprised to find themselves leading sixth-form assemblies.

Rehearsal is advised before any reading, and (in larger assemblies) some thought might be given as to who is the best available reader (or readers) for any particular passage. No matter how much at home you feel reading to the assembly, remember that even a professional actor or reader prefers to have time to rehearse – that is, to check that he or she understands the meaning of what is to be read, to absorb its mood and tone, to appreciate the writer's viewpoint, and to note where pauses and changes of pace are necessary.

For most passages, two introductions have been provided. The first (in italics) is a background note for the assembly leader's information. The second will serve as a ready-made introduction which can simply be read aloud to introduce the passage to the assembly when time does not permit the devising of a more locally relevant introduction.

The gathering together of a number of people for assembly places a heavy responsibility on those who lead that assembly. I hope this collection will lighten the load a little and help the arrangement of assemblies or even acts of worship that (1) nurture an awareness of the transcendental and the needs of others, (2) develop a sense of community and of what it means to be religious, and (3) create a feeling of wonder, mystery, joy and – yes – idealism.

DAVID SELF

FESTIVALS OF FAITH

'*A time to weep and a time to laugh*'
ECCLESIASTES

1

Happy New Year!

The Jewish New Year's Day is known as Rosh Hashanah and occurs in late September. Its exact date can be found in most diaries. For Jews, besides being the start of the New Year, it also commemorates God's creation of the world. This passage is the script of one of Rabbi Lionel Blue's Monday morning 'Thoughts for the Day' on BBC Radio 4.

Just when is New Year's Day? Most of you would probably say 1 January. But there are lots of different 'New Year's Days' – at different times of the year. For example, our school year begins in September. The Jews' New Year's Day will fall this year on . . .

For Jewish people, New Year's Day is a time to think of the things they have done wrong in the past year and to remember that God will judge each one of us. At this time of the year, Jews eat apple dipped in honey. The sharpness of the apple is a sign that we have done wrong, the honey is a sign of sweetness and hope for the coming year. Also at this time of the year, a musical instrument (a kind of ram's horn) called a 'shofar' is blown – as this passage, written by a Jewish rabbi, explains.

◆

IF YOU LIVE in a middle-class Jewish suburb, and it is late summer, you might be woken up before breakfast by a braying sound from your neighbour's garden. It is so shrill and so insistent, you might think it is the end of the world.

Well, for your Jewish neighbour it is – sort of. He has been practising on the ram's horn – 'an ill wind that no one blows good', in the words of the comedian Danny Kaye. No one blows it good because the horn is so ancient – it has no modern ☛

innards, no reed or whistle. I myself have never been able to coax a note out of it. But then I can't whistle either.

Although the liturgy for the Jewish New Year says, 'Happy the people, who hear this joyous sound', it sounds really more like an air raid alarm or an early warning system. Judgement, it says, is coming to everyone. All that you tried to hide in the last year from your neighbours, from your nearest and dearest, and especially from yourself is coming under review. You have a last chance to put everything right in the ten days after the New Year. Then comes the great Day of Atonement and the foretaste of your own last judgement.

Now this is not a cosy thought, and though there are a lot of sweet things to eat on the Jewish New Year, you can't help eating them rather thoughtfully. The pots of honey which Jewish people consume with slices of apple, or cooked with carrots and brisket, or mixed in honey cake cannot sweeten the terrible dilemmas of Jewish life.

Israel never loses a war, but can it ever win a real peace? The Palestinians in their camps look so much like Jews – but they are not Jews, are they? They are Palestinians. What happens if the political struggles of the Middle East join themselves to religious struggles and both together make a cocktail – one of those explosive cocktails you find in Northern Ireland – which make men drunk or mad? Will we Jews ever find a way to a Jewish life in a Marxist state or will the bitterness between us endure forever? Will the terrible cycle of Western life be repeated in our time – boom, slump and unemployment, pass the buck and Auschwitz? Why shouldn't it happen again? People haven't changed in the last forty years, have they?

But even these questions don't go deep enough, because they are about other people, living in other places at other times, ☞

and the New Year is not just about them, it is about me now. Not the masks life has taught me to wear, but the naked me stripped of my 'wardrobe of excuses'. It is terrifying to see yourself as you really are, and know yourself as the murderer and the victim, the oppressor and the oppressed, the manipulator who manipulates himself.

And all this goes through my mind on the Jewish New Year which celebrates the birthday of the world, as I meet my friends in their best clothes, and we eat honey cake together. That's the flavour of Jewish life and Jewish festivals, bitter-sweet, holding together happiness and insecurity, pride and shame, triumph and tragedy. ◆

RABBI LIONEL BLUE

2

Harvest

For centuries, people of all religions (and indeed of no religion) have chosen to give thanks once the crops have been gathered in – although the 'traditional' English parish church harvest festival service dates only from Victorian times. In recent years, this service has sometimes been adapted to become a thanksgiving for the produce of a particular locality – thus in a fishing port it may reflect the harvest of the seas.

This passage describes the Jewish harvest festival which is called Sukkot. Sukkot follows on from the autumn festivals of the Jewish New Year and Yom Kippur, which is also called the Day of Atonement (the holiest day of the year in the Jewish calendar). Sukkot is an eight-day festival during which families take their meals in huts or booths roofed with leafy branches and decorated with flowers and fruit. Note that the word 'Sukkot' is the name of the festival and also the plural of 'sukkah', which is an individual hut.

At this time of the year, all over the country, farmers will be finishing the job of gathering in the harvest. In some parts of the country it will be the fruit harvest, in others it will be the grain harvest. People have always wanted to say 'thank you' to God at harvest time, for what are sometimes called 'the fruits of the earth'. Jewish people celebrate harvest with an eight-day festival called Sukkot. In this passage, a Jewish teacher explains the meaning of Sukkot.

◆

IN ANCIENT DAYS, farmers lived in villages for protection and company. Every morning they went out to their fields and every evening they came home to their village.

But when the grapes were ripe and the wheat was heavy on the stalk, there was no time to go back and forth. The harvest ☛

could not wait. The grapes might start turning or a sudden storm might beat the heavy wheat to the ground. The harvesters worked from first light to first star. So they built little huts in the field in which to live during the harvesting. (Some Bedouin still do this today.)

These huts were called *sukkot*.

The harvest was a time of great thanksgiving. It was the time when man reaped the good things that his labour had produced. It was a time of feasting and giving joyful thanks to God for the food that had grown out of the earth, for that food meant life.

So the time of the harvest, when the people lived in sukkot, became a holiday that was also called Sukkot.

But for the Jew the holiday must have historical meaning, too. Pesah (or Passover) celebrates the Exodus out of Egypt. Sukkot continues the story. It marks the forty-year journey in the wilderness. For during that journey, tradition says, our ancestors escaped the sun by living in huts, or sukkot. These huts were put up as temporary shelters during their wandering. With God's help they survived. They did reach the Holy Land and permanent homes.

Of all the festivals, Sukkot has had to change most because we live so differently today than we used to. But the symbol of Sukkot is the sukkah, and every family is supposed to build one. In modern times it is difficult for many Jews to follow this commandment.

The Rabbis laid down specifications concerning the building of the sukkah. It must be no higher than 30 feet. It must have at least three walls. The roof must be of leaves and straw, with enough space so that the stars can be seen through the roof.

Building a sukkah has become a synagogue practice for many people rather than an individual family one. Every synagogue sets up a sukkah. Usually it is big and beautiful, with many kinds of fruit and vegetables as decorations. As part of the Sukkot celebration in the synagogue, everyone goes into the sukkah.

We may not really feel what it was like to live in huts as our ancestors did. But we can feel their faith and hope. Jews to this day manage to live through the most horrible times because they know that man and his world can become better – and will become better. How soon they become better depends partly on us. We are partners with God in creating that world. ◆

HARRY GERSH

3

Hallowe'en and All Saints' Day

In recent years, Hallowe'en has become a controversial festival. There is pressure from some quarters to ignore it altogether and it must be said that it can encourage an unhealthy interest in the occult. However, most children are aware of the festival anyway, and this passage is offered as an attempt to explain its origins and to show how Christianity has attempted to 'hallow' a once pagan celebration.

At your last school you may have celebrated Hallowe'en by painting pictures of witches or making paper masks and turnip lanterns – when you hollowed out turnips and put candles inside. There are many other traditions associated with this time of the year, such as bobbing for apples in a bucket of water (where you have to try to catch an apple with your teeth without using your hands at all). But what is the true meaning of this strange festival? And what has it got to do with the Christian festival of All Saints' Day, which follows on 1 November?

◆

THE DAY WE now know as Hallowe'en was, once upon a time, called Samhain. This was hundreds of years ago, before Christianity came to Britain.

Samhain marked the end of summer. It was when the herds of cattle were brought back from grazing in the fields to spend winter in the farm buildings. It was when laws were passed and when it was decided who would have the right to farm each piece of land during the following year.

This was because, in those days, Samhain was also New Year's ☞

Eve. It was celebrated with a fire festival, when bonfires were lit to scare away evil spirits. It was also thought that the souls of the dead came back to visit their homes at this time of the year.

But, as the centuries went by, Christians made what used to be the pagan New Year's Day (1 November) into a holy day, the Feast of All Saints. On this day, Christians began to remember all the good people who have lived in the past and who do not have their own special saint's day (like St David's Day or St Andrew's Day).

Even so, the older pagan customs continued to be observed the night before this 'new' holy day. This was partly because many people still believed in witchcraft, and witches (if you believed in them) were people to be feared. What's more, some people still thought that foul fiends ran wild on Hallowe'en – so, on this evening, some people actually prayed to the devil for protection and good fortune.

Our modern Hallowe'en owes much of its popularity to these old customs that were taken to America by Scottish and Irish emigrants. In the States, Hallowe'en became a night of mischief-making. In the last century, boys and young men went on orgies of vandalism. They overturned garden sheds, or set them on fire. They painted slogans on walls and broke windows for no good reason.

Another custom developed of children knocking on front doors and asking for sweets or 'cookies'. If they were given such a 'treat', they would not play a 'trick' – and so the night became known as 'trick or treat'. Today, some children still try playing 'tricks' – but some of the cakes or 'treats' recently given by angry American householders to tricksters have been found to contain razor blades and young children have been badly hurt. ☞

Although we no longer hold the beliefs that lie behind these Hallowe'en customs, these traditions are reminders of why the early Britons held their Samhain festival. They wanted to ward off the powers they feared and to protect their families and animals.

Christians do not believe, as these ancient Celts did, that the souls of the dead can harm us – although, as we have seen, it took hundreds of years for these beliefs to die out. But Christians do believe that people continue to live after death, when they come to a closer knowledge of God.

So Hallowtide (and especially All Saints' Day) is the time of year when Christians praise God for those people whose lives have provided a good example to us. Then, on All Souls' Day (2 November), they thank God for the lives of members of their families and for friends who have died. As a famous hymn puts it:

For all the saints who from their labours rest,
Who thee by faith before the world confessed,
Thy Name, O Jesus, be for ever blest.

4

Remembrance Sunday

Remembrance Sunday or Poppy Day can seem an awkward occasion to young people. All too easily, it can appear to glorify war or to be something that involves only the very old. Its purpose is of course to remind us of those who have lost their lives in war and those who still suffer its effects – whether they be from the two world wars or more recent conflicts such as those in the Falklands and the Gulf.

(Note: In the first poem in this 'mini-anthology', a soldier in the trenches is writing a letter to his wife at home. What he says aloud to his colleagues is printed in brackets. The title of the second poem is the beginning of a Latin proverb: 'It is sweet and fitting to die for one's country.')

This Sunday is Remembrance Sunday. On it we remember all those who lost their lives in the two world wars, and in more recent wars. Many people wear a poppy on this Sunday as a sign of remembrance. The money from the poppies goes to help those still alive who were wounded in the wars, and their families. Many people will keep a silence for two minutes on Sunday morning at 11 o'clock as a sign of respect.

A young person was once talking to an old man who had fought in one of the great wars. Hoping to please the old man he said, 'I suppose Remembrance Sunday is to remember those soldiers who gave their lives in the war.'

The old soldier was angry. 'Rubbish,' he snapped. 'Nobody gave anything. It was taken away in the crudest possible manner. That is what we should not forget.'

In this first poem, a Cockney soldier with the BEF (that is, the British Expeditionary force in the First World War) writes a letter home.

The Letter

    With BEF June 10. Dear Wife,
    (O blast this pencil. 'Ere, Bill, lend's a knife.)
    I'm in the pink at present, dear.
    I think the war will end this year.
    We don't see much of them square-'eaded 'Uns.
    We're out of harm's way, not bad fed.
    I'm longing for a taste of your old buns.
    (Say, Jimmie, spare's a bite of bread.)
    There don't seem much to say just now.
    (Yer what? Then don't, yer ruddy cow!
    And give us back me cigarette!)
    I'll soon be 'ome. You mustn't fret.
    My feet's improvin', as I told you of.
    We're out in rest now. Never fear.
    (VRACH! By crumbs, but that was near.)
    Mother might spare you half a sov.
    Kiss Nell and Bert. When me and you –
    (Eh? What the 'ell! Stand to? Stand to!
    Jim, give's a hand with pack on, lad.
    Guh! Christ! I'm hit. Take 'old. Aye, bad.
    No, damn your iodine. Jim? 'Ere!
    Write my old girl, Jim, there's a dear.)

WILFRED OWEN

Dulce Et Decorum Est

Bent double, like old beggars under sacks,
Knock-kneed, coughing like hags, we cursed through sludge,
Till on the haunting flares we turned our backs
And towards our distant rest began to trudge.
Men marched asleep. Many lost their boots
But limped on, blood-shod. All went lame; all blind;
Drunk with fatigue; deaf even to the hoots
Of tired, outstripped Five-Nines that dropped behind.

Gas! Gas! Quick, boys! – An ecstasy of fumbling,
Fitting the clumsy helmets just in time;
But someone still was yelling out and stumbling
And flound'ring like a man in fire or lime . . .
Dim, through the misty panes and thick green light,
As under a green sea, I saw him drowning.

In all my dreams, before my helpless sight,
He plunges at me, guttering, choking, drowning.

If in some smothering dreams you too could pace
Behind the wagon that we flung him in,
And watch the white eyes writhing in his face,
His hanging face, like a devil's sick of sin;
If you could hear, at every jolt, the blood
Come gargling from the froth-corrupted lungs,
Obscene as cancer, bitter as the cud
Of vile, incurable sores on innocent tongues, –
My friend, you would not tell with such high zest
To children ardent for some desperate glory,
The old Lie: Dulce et decorum est
Pro patria mori.

WILFRED OWEN ☞

For the Fallen (September 1914)

With proud thanksgiving, a mother for her children,
England mourns for her dead across the sea.
Flesh of her flesh they were, spirit of her spirit,
Fallen in the cause of the free.

Solemn the drums thrill: Death august and royal
Sings sorrow up into immortal spheres.
There is music in the midst of desolation
And a glory that shines upon our tears.

They went with songs to the battle, they were young,
Straight of limb, true of eye, steady and aglow.
They were staunch to the end against odds uncounted,
They fell with their faces to the foe.

They shall grow not old, as we that are left grow old:
Age shall not weary them, nor the years condemn.
At the going down of the sun and in the morning
We will remember them.

They mingle not with their laughing comrades again;
They sit no more at familiar tables of home;
They have no lot in our labour of the day-time:
They sleep beyond England's foam.

But where our desires are and our hopes profound,
Felt as a well-spring that is hidden from sight,
To the innermost heart of their own land they are known
As the stars are known to the Night;

As the stars that shall be bright when we are dust
Moving in marches upon the heavenly plain,
As the stars that are starry in the time of our darkness,
To the end, to the end, they remain.◆

LAURENCE BINYON

5

Christmas Customs

A description and explanation of the origins of some Christmas customs.

For many people, one of the great excitements of Christmas is putting up decorations. Nowadays, they may be made of plastic or paper and covered with glitter and tinsel. It wasn't always so.

◆

'ON CHRISTMAS EVE a great quantity of holly and of laurel is brought in from the garden and from the farm. This greenery is put up all over the house in every room just before it becomes dark on that day. Then there is brought into the hall a young pine tree, about twice the height of a man, to service for a Christmas tree, and on this innumerable little candles are fixed, and presents for all the household and the guests and the children of the village.'

That account by someone living a hundred years ago describes the custom of bringing a fir tree indoors and decorating it for Christmas. The custom originated in Germany – and it was Prince Albert, the German husband of Queen Victoria, who made it popular in Britain.

We have used holly, ivy and mistletoe, however, as decorations long before 'Christmas' trees. Because they are evergreens, they have always been symbols of eternal life, and mistletoe in particular was regarded as a sacred plant long before Christianity came to Britain. Indeed, it was said to cure everything from epilepsy to toothache – while holly was said to be a protection against fire and storms!

Another tradition is bringing home the yule log – yule being the name of a pagan festival celebrated at this time of the year in northern countries, long before the coming of Christianity!

> 'There is brought in a very large log of oak. This log of oak is the Christmas or Yule log and the rule is that it must be too heavy for one man to lift; so two men come, bringing it in from outside, the master of the house and his servant. They cast it down upon the fire in the great hearth of the dining-room, and the superstition is that, if it burns all night and is found still smouldering in the morning, the home will be prosperous for the coming year.'

Fire and candles were important to primitive peoples in the northern hemisphere. As the days got shorter, they were a reminder that light would soon return to the world. Indeed, some people thought that, by burning yule logs, they would give new strength to the dying sun. And when Christianity began to spread through Europe, it adopted many of these customs as a way of showing how Jesus brought light into a dark world. And such good news needed celebrating.

For many people, the ideal Christmas dinner is the one described by Charles Dickens at the end of his 'Christmas Carol' when Scrooge, now reformed, arranges for a splendid goose to be delivered to poor Bob Cratchit and his family . . .

> 'There never was such a goose. Bob said he didn't believe there ever was such a goose cooked. Its tenderness and flavour, size and cheapness, were the themes of universal admiration. Eked out by apple sauce and mashed potatoes, it was sufficient dinner for the whole family; indeed, as Mrs Cratchit said with great delight (surveying one small atom of a bone upon the dish), they hadn't ate it all at last! Yet everyone had had enough, and the youngest Cratchits in ☞

particular, were steeped in sage and onion to the eyebrows! But now, the plates being changed by Miss Belinda, Mrs Cratchit left the room alone – too nervous to bear witness – to take the pudding up and bring it in.

Suppose it should not be done enough! Suppose it should break in turning out! Suppose somebody should have got over the wall of the back-yard, and stolen it, while they were merry with the goose – a supposition at which the two young Cratchits became livid! All sorts of horrors were supposed.

Hallo! A great deal of steam! The pudding was out of the copper. A smell like a washing-day! That was the cloth. A smell like an eating-house and a pastrycook's next door to each other, with a laundress's next door to that! That was the pudding! In half a minute Mrs Cratchit entered – flushed, but smiling proudly – with the pudding, like a speckled cannon-ball, so hard and firm, blazing in half of half-a-quartern of ignited brandy, and bedecked with Christmas holly stuck into the top. Oh, a wonderful pudding! Bob Cratchit said, and calmly too, that he regarded it as the greatest success achieved by Mrs Cratchit since their marriage.' ◆

6

Christmas Mastermind

*By the time they have been through primary school, many children feel
they know every detail of the traditional Christmas story. In reality,
they may be quite hazy as to what the two Gospel accounts (Matthew
1.18—2.23; Luke 2) do or do not include. This passage, written as a
parody of the well-known television programme* Mastermind, *is a
reminder of the details of the birth of Jesus. Obviously it requires two
readers and will benefit from adequate rehearsal. The theme music of*
Mastermind *is available on a number of tapes and records: it is called
'Approaching Menace'.*

QUIZMASTER: And now our next contestant. Your name,
please?

NOEL: Noel Know-all.

Q.M.: And your chosen subject?

NOEL: 'The Christmas Story, as told in the Bible.'

Q.M.: Mr Know-all, you have two minutes on the Christmas
Story, as told in the Bible. Starting: now . . . . Of the four
accounts of the life of Jesus in the Bible, how many describe
his birth?

NOEL: All of them.

Q.M.: No, just two. The Gospels of Mark and John don't tell
the story of his birth. In which town did Joseph and Mary
live?

NOEL: Nazareth.

Q.M.: Yes. Nazareth in Galilee. In which town was Jesus born?

NOEL: [*Smug*] Bethlehem.

☛

Q.M.: In what sort of building was he born?

NOEL: [*Very smug*] A stable.

Q.M.: No, I can't accept that. The answer is we don't know. The Bible simply says Mary placed Jesus in a manger. It could have been anywhere. What was the weather like when he was born?

NOEL: Er . . . snowing?

Q.M.: No. It was mild enough for the shepherds to keep their sheep out on the hillside at night. What animals surrounded the baby Jesus?

NOEL: An ox. Er, and a donkey.

Q.M.: No, there's no mention of any animals in the Bible story. How many kings came to visit the baby Jesus?

NOEL: Three.

Q.M.: No, the answer's none. The Bible speaks of 'wise men' or 'magi' coming to him. How many wise men came to see him?

NOEL: [*Laughing*] Oh, three! Three!

Q.M.: No. Again, the Bible doesn't tell us. It simply says they gave him three gifts. When the wise men came to see the baby, in what sort –

[*Buzzer*]

Q.M.: I've started so I'll finish. When the wise men came to see the baby Jesus, in what sort of building was he?

NOEL: [*Long pause*] Must be a stable?

Q.M.: No. A house. Mr Know-all, on your specialist subject, 'The Christmas Story, as told in the Bible', you scored two points and no passes. ◆

7

What Are You Doing for Christmas?

A recent survey of 500 secondary school pupils suggested that what they liked best about Christmas was the 'build-up' period immediately before it. In second place came 'getting presents' and third was 'television'. The only other aspect to get a significant mention was food. The same survey revealed that only 15 per cent of pupils intended going to church even once over the Christmas period. These three anecdotes are offered by way of a challenge to older pupils – and as an encouragement to those who feel they have to justify their churchgoing.

At this time of year people often ask the question, 'What are you doing for Christmas?' For most people the answer will be 'buying presents', 'giving presents', 'getting presents' or 'watching television'. Another answer might be 'eating and drinking'. But what are *you* doing for Christmas – and why? This is a story about two eighteen-year-olds called Martin and Denzo.

◆

I WANT TO tell you about Martin and Denzo. Everyone calls him Denzo – although his real name's Peter Dennison. Anyway, Martin and Denzo have been best mates since they were in the same class in middle school.

Well, it was the Monday night just before Christmas and they were having a pint in the local. They're both eighteen, so that's all right. And they're making plans as to what they're doing over Christmas – like where to have a drink.

But Martin says he's not going out drinking on Christmas Eve 'cause he's going to the midnight church service and he wants to be sober for that.

Well, this sets Denzo off. It's the one thing they don't agree ☞

about. Martin goes to church quite regularly; Denzo – never. In fact, he's quite a lad; one girl after another and you don't ask where he gets the stuff he sells out of his father's car boot.

So he has a go at Martin. 'You're wasting your time, all this going to church. Behaving properly. Thinking about others. Look after number one, that's my motto.'

'Ah well, you see,' says Martin ('cause he's a thoughtful one), 'I grant you, if there is no God and heaven like you say, yeh, I have wasted quite a bit of time. But if *I'm* right, then you'll find you've wasted for ever. Cheers.'

<hr/>

And he drinks up. 'You buying?'

Come Boxing Day, Martin and Denzo were driving across to Nottingham – bit of a trek, but there was a concert they wanted to see.

Denzo has bought this secondhand car from a bloke he knows – so he's driving and the girls are in the back. Pat and Carol. And Pat's started wondering what she sees in Denzo 'cause he's so full of himself, and Carol's wondering what she sees in Martin 'cause he hardly says anything.

Anyway, they're on the A17 and this van comes right towards them, overtaking, their side of the road. Well, Denzo has to brake hard but it's all right except he starts teasing Martin. 'Say one of your prayers, did you?'

And then he tells Pat and Carol how Martin goes to church. Confession an' everything.

But Martin speaks up, says yes he does. He believes God forgives him. For what he does wrong.

Denzo just laughs. 'Tell you what, if God does forgive people, ☞

why waste time being good? I'll just enjoy myself and say sorry the minute I die.'

'Oh yeh?' says Martin. 'That's what you say now. Suppose you forget? Or there's an accident and you don't get time? Then what?' They're all a bit quiet then. Except Pat says Martin had better drive on the way back if Denzo's going to drink.

◆

It was New Year's Day. Martin and Denzo were in their local. I told you how Denzo's real name is Peter Dennison but everyone calls him Denzo? And that they're good mates, except Denzo goes on at Martin a bit 'cause Martin goes to church.

Anyway, it's New Year's Day dinner time and Martin's wondering if Denzo's not really sobered up after the night before 'cause he's wanting to talk about when you die and whether you really do have to stand at the gates of heaven while St Peter or someone looks you up in a great big book to see whether they'll let you in.

Well, Martin says no one really knows what it'll be like and waits for Denzo to say what he usually says – like 'If that's so, why waste your time trying to be good?'

But he doesn't. Denzo's had this idea. 'Perhaps it's a bit like how those communist countries used to be. Where it was a crime to be a Christian and the police collected evidence to try to prove people were secret Christians.'

'And it'll be like that when you get to heaven,' he goes on. 'St Peter'll look in his big book and see if there's enough evidence to prove you've been a proper Christian – and he'll only let you in if there is.'

And this time it's Martin's turn to feel uneasy. So he thinks for a bit and then he says, 'Same again?' ◆

8

St *Valentine's* Day *(14 February)*

A reading for St Valentine's Day, explaining its traditions.

Today, you don't need me to remind you, is St Valentine's Day. But who was St Valentine?

Well, he was a priest. He lived in Rome hundreds of years ago (in the third century) and, because he helped some Christians who were going to be put to death by an evil dictator (the Emperor Claudius), he was put in prison. While he was in there, he healed the chief warder's daughter who had problems with her sight – and the warder and all his family became Christians.

When Emperor Claudius heard this, he lost his temper and said Valentine should be executed. And so, on 14 February around the year 270, Valentine was clubbed to death. And then his head was chopped off, just to make sure.

A nice romantic story, isn't it?

So why then do we send Valentine's Day cards? Well, simply because it's said that this is also the day of the year that marks the start of the mating season for birds – and I mean the feathered kind. Which *does* make it a romantic occasion.

And there was an ancient custom of sending your true love a present on Valentine's Day. Nowadays, of course, it's more usual to send a greetings card than a present – but a few lucky people might get a box of chocolates or even a bunch of red roses.

But today might also be a suitable day for remembering, more seriously, all those (like Valentine) who are now suffering or imprisoned for their beliefs – because of dictators like Claudius. ◆

9

Shrove Tuesday and Ash Wednesday

*Shrove Tuesday (or Pancake Day) is the day before Ash Wednesday, the
first day of Lent. Its date varies according to the date of Easter, with
Lent being the period of forty days that leads up to Easter Sunday.*

*For Christians, Lent has traditionally been a time of fasting.
Shrovetide was therefore a period of celebration and carnival before the
fast when the last of any food that would not keep during the period of
Lent was eaten up. Until the Reformation Shrovetide lasted for a week
or more. Shrove Tuesday is observed as Mardi Gras in France and
America, as Fasching in Germany, and as Carnival (from the Latin
carne vale: 'farewell to meat') in Trinidad and Tobago.*

At this time of the year in the West Indian islands of Trinidad
and Tobago there are processions, steel bands, dances and
fancy dress parades through the streets. It is perhaps the most
exciting festival of the year – but how do we celebrate Shrove
Tuesday in Britain?

◆

Shrove Tuesday

'Fat Tuesday' doesn't sound much of a day, does it? But that's
what today is called in some countries. Put it in French and it
sounds a bit better. 'Mardi Gras' – a day when 'anything goes'
in some American cities where they have carnival processions
and fancy dress parades. And, as I said, in the West Indies there
is feasting and singing and dancing till all hours.

And what do we get up to in this country? Well, we pour some
batter in a frying pan, cook it, and lob it in the air. Yes, we call it
Pancake Day.

But why do all these customs take place? The point is that ☞

today is the last day before Lent, a period of forty days when people used to fast, to go without certain kinds of food. And so, on the Tuesday before Lent started, in those days when there were no fridges or freezers, they used up all the milk and eggs and fat that wouldn't keep till the end of Lent. So it got the name 'Fat Tuesday' or Mardi Gras.

Its other name is Shrove Tuesday. 'Shrove' comes from an old English word, *shriven,* which meant to be forgiven of your sins. On this day people used to go to church to confess the things they'd done wrong – and then the priest would 'shrive' them. Even today, it's quite a good time for saying sorry for anything we've done wrong – as well as for eating pancakes.

Ash Wednesday

Today is quite a good day for staring at people's foreheads. Honestly!

It's because it's Ash Wednesday – which is nothing to do with cigarette ash, but more to do with sackcloth and ashes. Sackcloth and ashes because, back in biblical times, people who wanted to admit how sinful or wicked they'd been would go around dressed only in old sacking – and they'd also cover themselves with ashes.

Well, no one does that nowadays – except that some Christians do go to church today to have a tiny smudge of ashes put on their foreheads.

Where this happens (and it's mainly in Roman Catholic and some Church of England churches), the priest first of all burns some of the palm crosses that have been kept from last year's Palm Sunday, and then he mixes the ashes with a little water to make a kind of greyish paste.

Then, when people come to church on Ash Wednesday, he dips his thumb in the paste and marks a cross on their forehead.

As in olden times, it's a sign that they've done wrong – and are owning up to that fact. It can take courage to humble yourself in public. Which is why (on Ash Wednesday) it's a kind of strength, not weakness, to go around with a dirty forehead. ◆

10

Mothering Sunday

*Mothering Sunday occurs in the middle of the Christian season of Lent.
The secular Mother's Day is observed on the second Sunday of May,
except in this country where it has been superimposed on Mothering
Sunday. This passage is an explanation of how the two days have
become confused and of the meaning of a day which is also sometimes
known as Refreshment Sunday (a minor feast in the middle of the fast of
Lent).*

*The explanation of Mothering Sunday is followed by a poem which
describes how young girls 'in service' or sons who had been sent away to
be apprenticed to a craftsman returned home to see their mothers on this
day of the year and the poem is written as if it is being spoken by one
such daughter. The food traditionally associated with Mothering
Sunday is simnel cake (the poem refers to the less usual 'wheaten cake' in
verse 3).*

Cards, a bunch of flowers or a box of chocolates; which will
you be buying this weekend and why?

◆

YOU MAY THINK Sunday's Mother's Day. It's not.
Mother's Day is not for another two months. Honestly!

Mother's Day was started back in 1907 by an American, a Miss
Anna Jarvis of Philadelphia. After her mother died, she felt a
day should be set aside on which people should give thanks for
their mothers. The American government made it official and
since then the second Sunday in May has been called Mother's
Day.

But America's Mother's Day isn't quite the same as our
'Mothering Sunday' (which is this Sunday). Mothering
Sunday goes back much further to when village people made a ☞

point of going not to their local church, but to the nearest big church – to what they called the 'Mother Church'. Mothering Sunday was a day on which Christians gave thanks for 'Mother Church'.

But in the days when there were no real holidays, this particular Sunday also became a day when children who'd moved away (to work as servants in big houses or as apprentices) were given time off to visit their mothers.

In this country, we've mixed up the American Mother's Day and the English Mothering Sunday – and we celebrate both this weekend. So whichever we celebrate, it *is* a day for being grateful for what's special about Mum – but for some, it's also a day for being grateful for 'Mother Church' and what *it's* done for us over the centuries.

Mothering Sunday

It is the day of all the year,
Of all the year the one day,
When I shall see my mother dear
And bring her cheer,
A-mothering on Sunday.

So I'll put on my Sunday coat,
And in my hat a feather,
And get the lines I writ by rote,
With many a note,
That I've a-strung together.

And now to fetch my wheaten cake,
To fetch it from the baker,
He promised me, for mother's sake,
The best he'd bake
For me to fetch and take her.

Well have I known, as I went by
One hollow lane, that none day
I'd fail to find – for all they're shy –
Where violets lie,
As I went home on Sunday.

My sister Jane is waiting-maid
Along with Squire's lady;
And year by year her part she's played,
And home she stayed,
To get the dinner ready.

For mother'll come to church, you'll see –
Of all the year it's the day –
'The one,' she'll say, 'that's made for me.'
And so it be:
It's every mother's free day.

The boys will all come home from town,
Not one will miss that one day;
And every maid will bustle down
To show her gown,
A-mothering on Sunday.

It is the day of all the year,
Of all the year the one day;
And here come I, my mother dear,
To bring you cheer,
A-mothering on Sunday. ◆

GEORGE HARE LEONARD

11

Holi

Holi is a Hindu festival that occurs at the start of India's hot season in either late February or March. It celebrates the Lord Krishna's love of amorous jokes and games and is a time for carnivals, processions and dances. Barriers of caste and rank are forgotten as people throw coloured water and bright powders at each other. Students have licence to chase their teachers down the street and workers spray their employers with water. The evening is a time for visiting and exchanging of sweets and gifts. (The festival of Holi is also celebrated by Sikhs.)

(Note: This passage may be shortened by simply reading the first section and the conclusion.)

Throughout the northern half of the world the spring months see many celebrations of the return of light and new life to the world after the gloom of winter. At this time of the year in India people celebrate the Hindu festival of Holi. As you'll hear, this is not the time of year to wear new clothes!

◆

IF YOU HAPPENED to be visiting India at the beginning of March, during the month called Phalguna, you would be well advised to stay inside on the day after the full moon, especially if you are the sort of person who doesn't like practical jokes. As soon as you walked out into the street you would be soaked to the skin from repeated attacks by groups of children and young men, shrieking, 'Holi hai, Holi hai'. They drench passers-by with buckets of coloured water, or use bicycle pumps to squirt red, yellow and green sprays over everyone within range. Balloons filled with water are hurled over walls and through open windows. Every kind of mischief is played, and handful after handful of multicoloured dust is thrown into the air. It is ☞

all very good humoured and, if you enjoy a water fight, there is nothing to stop you joining in and giving back as good as you get. This is Holi, the Festival of Colours, the tumultuous, riotous celebration that ends the Indian year. Everybody is out to have a good time and the three essential elements of the festival are 'rang, ras and rag' – colour, dance and song. The spirit of Holi is foolery and those who are pompous and self-important are shown little mercy at the hands of the merrymakers.

India is a vast country and Holi customs vary, but in most areas huge bonfires are lit. Streets, parks and all public places are crowded with people daubed with colour, clapping, shouting, singing and dancing. They have horns, drums and cymbals and make an unbelievable din. Often all this noise and excitement accompanies a spectacular religious procession swaying its way through the streets with one or more statues held aloft on decorated platforms, surrounded by priests and worshippers.

The night before

On the day before the night of the full moon people fast in preparation for the festival, but as dusk falls a priest lights the bonfire, says a special prayer, and the celebrations begin. Crowds gather to watch as men and boys dance around the flames, even attempting to jump over or through them, often smearing themselves with the ashes. Drums are beaten, horns blown, accompanied by singing, loud shouts and cries.

In areas where the spring crops are ready for harvesting, it is usual to make offerings of those crops to God, by placing them on the fire. Barley is roasted in the ashes and then eaten. In some places wheat cakes stuffed with gram (chick-peas) and ☞

sugar are thrown into the blaze and, in others, ears of wheat and gram are tied to sugar-cane and dipped into the flames. Coconuts are roasted as they are a symbol of fertility. Some people take home a flaming brand or a little pot of glowing ash in order to light their own fires at home from the Holi fire.

The power of dance

In the evening when the excitement of the day dies down, people change into clean clothes. They may assemble in a park or public place to eat together and gossip to the accompaniment of a play, singing, or local folk-dances. Throughout India the power of dance to tell a story is much appreciated and loved. It is one of the most popular ways in which to watch the stories of the gods being told.

Different areas have varying styles of dancing. One of the best known is part of the celebrations in and around the town of Mathura. Called the 'Ras Lila', it is a dance in honour of the early life of the god Krishna. Another custom in this region is the setting up of flower-decorated swings to recall the suspended cradle of the baby Krishna.

Fairs, and even circuses, are often a part of festival celebrations. In the Punjab, Holi fairs are enormous and go on for many days. They can attract up to ten thousand people.

Conclusion

In many parts of the world the end of winter and the beginning of spring is something that people look forward to. It seems to bring with it feelings of cheerfulness and hope and in many countries, as in India, it is the time at which a new year begins. Although their winters are not as cold as ours, Indians are still glad when they are over. For farmers especially it is an ☞

important time. Wheat and barley are ripening and the first harvest of the year will soon begin. In the month of Phalguna, spring is at its height in India, and people seem to catch the exhilarating atmosphere. Although Holi is primarily a Hindu festival, it is a great carnival in which everybody takes part. ◆

JANIS HANNAFORD

12

Holy Week

The major Christian festival of the year is Easter. In the week preceding it, Christians remember the events of Jesus' last week before his crucifixion. That week began with his triumphal entry into Jerusalem on Palm Sunday and included his institution of Holy Communion on the evening of the Thursday – followed by his arrest and execution. These two passages take the form of radio news reports that might have been filed by an objective reporter from Jerusalem during that week. The first could have been broadcast on either the Tuesday or Wednesday; the second report might have been filed sometime around midnight on the Thursday night or early on the morning of the first Good Friday.

Think what it's like to be invaded. An occupying army in every street and every pub. Just like *'Allo 'Allo*, but without the jokes.

That's roughly how it was when Jesus was alive. His country, Palestine, had been occupied by the Romans. Suppose we could hear a political correspondent of those days, reporting from Jerusalem during the week leading up to the first Easter day . . .

◆

WELL, HERE IN Jerusalem, as you know, the Roman Army is in control. Because the city is crowded with visitors for the Jewish Passover Festival, the Roman area governor, Pontius Pilate, is making one of his rare visits to the city and staying in what used to be King Herod's Royal Palace.

The Romans have allowed the Jewish leaders to continue in office, though they have no real power. Among them, the Sadducee Party has a two-thirds majority over the Pharisees. Most Sadducees are committed to defending the interests of ☛

wealthy and aristocratic Jewish families, while the so-called 'kill-joy' Pharisees are much stricter in the way they interpret the law.

Meanwhile, the Zealot Revolutionary Party is keen to oust the Romans – by violence if necessary. Under government reporting restrictions we are not allowed to interview any member of the Zealot Party, but among their number is a man called Judas Iscariot.

He's said also to follow a wandering preacher called Jesus. Some people think Jesus may join the Zealot revolutionaries; others say not. He's very popular with the people, unpopular with both political parties and, so far, ignored by the Romans. Further reports in later bulletins.

This is . . . , reporting from Jerusalem.

On Maundy Thursday (the Thursday before Easter) Christians remember how Jesus was arrested the night before his crucifixion on Good Friday. Suppose we were able to hear a news report from Jerusalem nearly 2,000 years ago . . .

———————————— ◆ ————————————

Here in Jerusalem, Jewish leaders are asking the Roman governor, Pontius Pilate, to sentence to death a Galilean preacher known as Jesus from Nazareth.

He was arrested earlier tonight and is the leader of a new religious movement which, over the last three years, has attracted literally hundreds of followers.

The Jewish authorities are accusing Jesus of stirring up trouble by claiming to be 'King of the Jews'. But the Jewish leaders are secretly much more concerned about his fast-growing religious movement, which they regard as dangerous.

Some witnesses have been found who accuse Jesus of ☛

offending the name of God and of threatening to destroy the Temple, the most holy building in the city for all Jews.

Jesus was arrested tonight in a garden called Gethsemane just outside the city walls. One of his former friends led the temple police to him. After a brief scuffle, a group of his companions fled. An unconfirmed report has come in that Jesus healed the ear of a man which had been cut off during the struggle. Jesus is at present under guard and refusing to answer any questions put to him.

Religious charges do not carry the death penalty, but if he is found guilty of treason against the Roman state, then that crime would of course attract an automatic death sentence, by crucifixion.

This is . . . , reporting from Jerusalem. ◆

13

Good Friday (1)

This passage attempts to explain the circumstances of the crucifixion of Jesus Christ. It is written in the form of a radio news bulletin.

Good Friday is the day when Christians remember how Jesus was put to death on the cross. But exactly what went on in Jerusalem all those years ago? If radio had existed then, what would have been on the local news?

◆

EARLY THIS MORNING, the Roman governor of Judea, His Excellency Pontius Pilate, gave permission for the execution of the teacher and alleged revolutionary, Jesus of Nazareth. He also announced the release from prison of a man called Barabbas, condemned to death for the brutal murder of a group of Roman soldiers.

The announcement of the death sentence on Jesus of Nazareth came as something of a surprise as, earlier, the governor had spoken to the crowds outside the imperial palace and said that he could see no reason to find him guilty.

The crowds made no secret of their anger at this statement and later the new decision was announced. Jesus was immediately led away to be whipped and crucified according to Roman tradition. Large crowds followed him through the streets to the hill known as Golgotha to the north-west of the city. He is now nailed to the cross: death is not expected for some hours.

And now the main points of the rest of the news.

The Zealots, the revolutionary movement fighting for the ☞

removal of all Romans from Judea, have welcomed the release of Barabbas. A spokesman said, 'We could not have had better news at this holy season of the year.'

Preparations for the Jewish feast of Passover go ahead throughout the city. The festival begins at six o'clock tonight.

And lastly, weathermen have no explanation for the unnatural darkness that began about an hour ago. As listeners in Jerusalem will know, at the moment it is hardly light enough outside to read a scroll.

More news: in your Bible. ◆

14

Good Friday (2)

These two short passages attempt to fill in some of the details behind the crucifixion of Jesus and to give pupils an awareness of its horror and importance.

How quickly can you work out who this is?

———————————————— ◆ ————————————————

HE WAS BORN in Spain. Very rich. The family had property worth half a million. He bought himself into an outfit known as the Knights of the Cavalry, the Ordo Equester. A sort of roving upper-class gang who did a little unofficial police work for the state.

Then he married. Married very nicely. She was called Claudia Procula, the illegitimate daughter of the third wife of the future emperor. Very *Dynasty,* very *Dallas.*

Except that this was 2,000 years ago. And he was called Pontius Pilate, the man who sentenced Jesus to death by crucifixion.

Around the year AD 26 he was made governor of part of the Roman Empire: the area around Jerusalem.

He was described as being greedy, vindictive and cruel. And that was just what his friends said.

When he got to Jerusalem, he proved a dab hand at upsetting the locals. Like when he built them a new water supply system – and then raided the Holy Temple for cash to pay for it. When a mob got angry, he had his soldiers disguise themselves as locals, move into the crowd and, on a given signal, produce ☞

hefty clubs and hit the protesters to death with them. Just like that.

Then came the episode of Jesus of Nazareth. During the trial, his wife sent him a message. 'Have nothing to do with this innocent man,' she said. And what did Pilate say? 'How many times have I told you not to call me at work?' No, he didn't say that. He tried to take her advice. Cruel, brutish Pontius Pilate who didn't give a damn wanted to set Jesus free. So what made a man like that think Jesus was worth saving?

Crucifixion

Crucifixion was the standard means of execution used by the Romans back in Bible times. How exactly did they do it?

First, the victim was whipped with a special kind of whip which had sharpened pieces of metal or bone fixed into the lash. All the better to draw blood with.

Then he had to carry his own cross to where he was to be executed. Not the whole thing, just the crosspiece. The upright was kept in place, handy for whenever it was needed. Mind you, the beam was heavy enough, especially on a hot day and if you were already losing blood from a whipping.

When everyone was ready, the victim was nailed to the crossbeam. Not through the palms of his hand. That wouldn't work because when you were heaved upright, the nails would tear through your flesh and out between your fingers. No; he was nailed through the wrist or lower arm. Then he and the crosspiece were hauled up and fixed to the upright.

The cross sometimes had a tiny ledge on it. If the victim had the strength, he could heave himself up, to half sit on it and ☞

take a bit of weight off his arms. This could delay death (and prolong the agony) for anything up to a few days. The choice was yours. Death eventually occurred through loss of blood, heart failure or suffocation (caused by the body's weight being taken on the arms). ◆

15

Easter Customs

A recent survey revealed that only one-third of the population had any idea of the religious significance of Easter. For the majority, it is simply 'something to do with eggs'. Or, as one person put it, 'Oh, you mean Chocolate Sunday!' The aim of this passage is to consider the significance of some of the secular Easter customs and their relationship to the festival of Easter. It may be used either before or after the festival, as seems most appropriate.

Easter is first of all a Christian festival. For Christians, indeed, Easter Sunday is the most important day of the year – but there are now many customs associated with the festival of Easter.

◆

FIRST, YOU CAN'T imagine Easter happening at any time but the spring, can you? Easter is obviously a spring festival – unless of course you live in Australia, where it occurs in the autumn.

Even though Easter is observed right around the world, the ways in which people celebrate it are linked to European customs; and what is particularly surprising is how little these customs vary from one country to another. Easter candles, Easter eggs, Easter bonnets and Easter parades or processions: they happen in Battersea and Bulgaria, in Malta and Moscow.

For centuries, people have celebrated the return of spring, with its signs of new growth, warmer days and the return of light to a world darkened by winter.

Partly because of this, the Romans used to celebrate their New Year's Day on 1 March and, to mark the occasion, a holy flame was lit in the temple of the goddess Vesta (she was goddess of ☞

the domestic hearth and is remembered today as a brand of matches!). When Christianity came along, it borrowed this custom and many other pagan customs associated with this time of year.

For example, whole communities in Greece make their way to the village church late on the Saturday night before Easter Day. Everyone takes an unlit candle (and schoolboys bring fireworks as well). The whole church is in darkness and crowded with people. As midnight approaches, the priest reads the Easter story from the Bible and, as he gets to the point where the Gospel tells how Jesus rose from the dead, a new flame is struck (traditionally from a flint on stone) and a candle is lit. Then the priest invites the people 'to share the never-setting light' and the flame is passed from candle to candle. When everyone's candle is alight, he cries out, 'Christos Anesti!' ('Christ is Risen'). Everyone holds their candle high and there is much embracing and joyful celebration – and later, fireworks.

Just as the Romans celebrated the new light of spring, so Greek Christians celebrate the belief that, although the world seemed dark and hopeless after the crucifixion, light, life and hope returned to the world at Easter with the resurrection of Jesus.

Similar services were held in this country in the Middle Ages. As an act of faith, people put out all lamps and fires before going to the Easter service (with an unlit candle). New light would be kindled in the church, and the candles lit and taken home (with great care if it was windy). Services like this are still held in many Roman Catholic churches and some Anglican ones. Often a very large candle is lit in the church and this is known as the Paschal candle.

'Paschal' is another word for Easter. It is derived from the ☞

Hebrew word *Pesach* meaning Passover and most European names for Easter come from this word: *Paques* (French), *Pascua* (Spanish), *Paach* (Dutch) and *Pask* (Swedish). The English word 'Easter' comes from a Saxon festival dedicated to the goddess of spring, Eostre.

Especially associated with Eostre is the animal the hare, and even today in Germany (and other parts of northern Europe, including Britain) children get up on Easter morning to look for what *Oster Hase* (Easter Hare) has hidden in the garden (or indoors, if wet).

Easter Hare (or, more realistically, parents) always hides Easter eggs. Nowadays these are usually chocolate ones, but traditionally they were real eggs, often decorated with intricate patterns. Even before the time of Jesus, people gave each other eggs as a springtime gift – a sign of new life returning to the world. For Christians, eggs can have a special meaning. An egg may look dead, but new life can break out of it – just as Jesus broke out of the tomb in which his body had been buried.

In Russian churches, wooden eggs bearing the initials for 'Christ is Risen' are thrown by the priests to the congregations. Some Russian eggs unscrew to reveal a succession of smaller eggs nestling one inside another.

Many games are played with eggs at Easter. In Greece and in northern England children play a game a bit like conkers. The egg is held firmly in the fist and knocked against an opponent's egg to see whose is the stronger and which egg can score most victories. In Northumberland it is called 'jarping' and in Cumbria it is known as 'dumping'. It must of course be played with hard-boiled eggs.

Egg-rolling games are also common in many countries, especially in Scotland and again in northern England. ☛

Coloured hard-boiled eggs (nowadays decorated with felt-pen patterns) are rolled down a slope until the shells break. The game is also played every year on the lawns of the White House in Washington, the grounds of which are opened to the public on Easter Mondays.

Just as widespread is the idea of an Easter procession. It may be a religious one in which holy statues or an empty cross is carried through the streets, or a more secular one which is simply a way of celebrating a bank holiday and of showing off new clothes. New clothes indicate a new start, and not to make a new start at Easter has always been considered unlucky:

At Easter let your clothes be new
Of else be sure you will it rue! ◆

16

Baisakhi

Baisakhi is both a Hindu and Sikh festival. It is usually celebrated on or near to 13 April. At this time Sikhs celebrate the 'birthday' of the Khalsa, the brotherhood of all Sikh men and women. This dates from when the tenth and last guru summoned the Sikhs to Anandpur. It is from this date that the Sikhs have worn their 'uniform' of uncut hair (covered with a turban), comb, bracelet, shots and sword.

Around this time of the year, Sikhs celebrate their most important annual festival. It recalls a day in the year 1699 when the last of the ten Sikh gurus (or teachers) summoned the Sikhs together at a place in India called Anandpur and there asked them to make a remarkable sacrifice.

◆

IN INDIA, THE wheat and grain are ready for harvesting in the month called Baisakhi – which is roughly the time of year it's April in this country. But just before the Sikhs in India start the work of gathering in the crops, they have always met together for a festival.

So it was almost 300 years ago, in 1699, in the town of Anandpur. This was in the time of the tenth Sikh guru (or leader) who was called Guru Gobind Rai.

As usual, the crowds gathered in front of his tent, expecting there to be prayers and singing of hymns. But after a while, the guru came out of his tent, wearing a bright new saffron-yellow tunic tied with a blue sash and also a turban to cover his hair. In his hand, he held a sword.

'This is not how it usually is,' muttered one or two of the ☛

crowd, but they quickly became quiet as the guru began to speak.

'By my sword,' said Guru Gobind Rai, 'I ask if there's one among you who will prove his faith by giving me . . . his head? Who will offer up his life?'

Now the Sikhs had plenty of enemies in India at that time, but they never expected it would be one of their own leaders who would want to take their life.

Not surprisingly, there was a long silence. Then the guru asked again, 'If there be any true Sikh here, let him offer up his head as proof of his faith.'

And from out of the crowd, a warrior Sikh from Lahore stepped forward. He was called Daya Ram and he spoke out bravely. 'My guru and my lord. My humble head is yours, if so you wish it.'

The guru led him into a tent. There was a moment's silence and then, from inside the tent, there came a dull thud. Then the guru came out with his sword, which was now dripping blood. Immediately he spoke again. 'If there be another true Sikh, let him now offer me his head as proof of his faith.'

This time a very poor farmer, Dharam Das from Delhi, came forward. 'If it's your will, then I will follow,' he murmured. Guru Gobind Rai led him into the tent. Again a thud was heard. Again, the guru reappeared with his sword dripping blood. And again he asked for the head of a Sikh.

This time it was a poor washerman from Gujerat who volunteered, a man called Mukham Chand. He too was led into the tent; a thud was heard and the guru reappeared with his sword now bloodier than ever.

Not surprisingly, some of the crowd had begun to edge quietly away. But what *was* surprising was that a fourth and fifth Sikh stepped forward when the guru asked for yet more men to offer up their lives to prove their faith.

But after the fifth Sikh had entered the tent and a fifth thud had been heard, there was a longer silence, and then Guru Robind Rai came out of his tent – followed by the five Sikhs who had offered up their lives! All were now dressed like the guru in yellow robes, tied with blue sashes – and each was wearing a turban.

'Behold my five brothers,' said the guru to the crowds who remained. 'These five have passed the hardest test, the test of faith – and they shall be known as the Khalsa, the pure ones. They are soldier saints who will spread abroad the Sikh message of brotherhood and sisterhood.'

And from that time, male Sikhs have not cut their hair; instead they have kept it clean and tidy, fastened with a comb under their turbans. And also from that day, male Sikhs have always worn a steel bracelet as a sign of the one God; and also a tiny sword – as a sign that they are ready to obey the teaching of their faith at all times, just as did the Khalsa that day in Anandpur. ◆

17

Ascensiontide

*Ascension Day is one of the three great festivals of the Christian year,
along with Christmas and Easter. It is still marked with a holiday in
many European countries, though its observance in Britain is now
minimal. It occurs forty days after Easter Sunday and marks the end of
the period in which Jesus Christ appeared to the disciples on a number of
occasions following his resurrection.*

*The Bible accounts of the Ascension of Jesus (in Luke's Gospel and the
Acts of the Apostles) cause modern Christians some problems. For
example, how literally should the story be taken?*

*One of the key elements of the Ascension for Christians today is its
message that Christ is the King of the World and that he promised his
followers that they would not be left 'comfortless'; instead, he would
send them the Holy Spirit to guide and strengthen them.*

*Christians commemorate the coming of the Holy Spirit ten days later
at Pentecost, also known as Whit Sunday. This passage from a novel by
Lloyd C. Douglas imagines what happened to the disciples in that period
between the first Ascension Day and the first Whit Sunday.*

You'll perhaps remember that one of the followers of Jesus was
a man called Peter who had previously been a fisherman. There
is a novel about him in which he is nicknamed 'The Big Fisherman', and in which the writer imagines what happened to the
disciples as they followed Jesus in Palestine almost 2,000 years
ago.

This particular passage describes how, after Jesus had been
crucified, the disciples believed he came back to life and talked
to them on a number of occasions. One was when the
disciples returned from fishing and found that Jesus was
cooking breakfast for them beside the lake.

THE SKY WAS brightening a little and the fog was dissolving. Dimly the outlines of the wharves and huts became visible. The Big Fisherman's narrowed eyes slowly swept the shoreline. A tall, slender column of blue smoke was rising from a small, bright fire at the water's edge. Beside the fire, warming his hands, stood the Master. He raised his arm, waved a hand, and called:

'Peter!'

Half an hour later the disciples began to arrive, by twos and threes, for the day's work. They hurried to the spot where Jesus and Peter sat side by side before the fire, and were greeted by the Master's welcoming smile. The Big Fisherman's shaggy head was wet; he was bare to the waist; his shirt lay near-by on the sand, drying. His eyes were red and swollen with weeping, but strangely luminous. It was plain to see what had happened. Peter had tearfully repented his weakness and had been fully restored to the Master's comradeship.

Thad and John ran to the live-box and returned with fish for breakfast, which they broiled over the fire, and produced wheaten bread from their well-filled baskets. The hour that followed was memorable. In a few days, the Master said, he would return home to his Father's House and leave them to continue his work.

Eventually he would revisit the world. In the meantime, they who believed in him – 'and they who will believe in me through your testimony' – would receive many indubitable evidences of his spiritual presence.

'Can you tell us when to expect your return, Master?' asked Philip.

'No one knows the day, nor the hour, Philip,' replied Jesus. 'What I say unto you, you may say unto all – Watch!'

In a quiet voice he gave them instructions for their movements in the days immediately before them. No more fishing now: their fishing days were over. They were to return to Jerusalem and await further orders. With that, he rose, held his outstretched hands over them in blessing, and said tenderly, 'My peace be with you.' They had all bowed their heads while the touching words were spoken; and when, at length, they lifted their eyes, he was gone.

For a long moment they sat stunned to silence. Peter was the first to rise. They all came to their feet and gathered about him, their questing eyes fixed on his sober face. No one needed to inquire which, among them, was appointed to be their leader. Peter had suddenly acquired maturity. His resonant voice, when he spoke, had a tone of authority.

'We will proceed to Jerusalem,' said Peter. 'James, John, and Thaddeus, you will row out to the ships, stow the nets, and secure the hatches. Then you will return home and prepare for your journey. The rest of us will go to our homes and say farewell to our families.'

Making their headquarters [in Jerusalem] at the shop of the old weaver Ben-Josef, the disciples restlessly awaited their summons. At length it was announced that they were to assemble on a near-by hill-top in the early morning of the twenty-fourth day of Iyar.

In obedience, they went singly up the long hill where the Master met them, and, after a few enheartening words, instructed them to remain in Jerusalem until they received further tidings.

Then they all knelt while he prayed for them; and when they arose from their knees, he was gone. Nor did they ever see him again, though – to the end of their days – they were constantly on the alert for his return. ◆

LLOYD C. DOUGLAS

18

Father's Day
(The third Sunday in June)

Father's Day is almost entirely a commercial invention whereby the manufacturers of greetings cards and other items have successfully 'cashed in' on the success of Mother's Day. Nevertheless, it is fitting that there should be an occasion when children learn to be grateful for their fathers.

However, it is a sad fact that a large number of families are one-parent units and it is often the father who is absent. But even in two-parent families, children often feel that their father is a somewhat distant character. This excerpt from an American novel describes not Father's Day itself, but a day on which a school holds an open day for fathers – who may attend classes and see how their children are progressing. It is offered in the hope that young people may see that it takes two sides to develop a relationship.

This Sunday is Father's Day. Not everyone gets on well with their father. This is part of a story about an American boy called Bobby. His father George Adams is always very busy and has little time for him. However, Bobby's mother persuades him to attend a school event called 'Father's Day', when fathers are invited to attend school lessons to see how their children are getting on . . .

◆

GEORGE ADAMS FINISHED his coffee, mashed out his cigarette in the saucer, and stood up.

'I'm off,' he said to his wife as he went to the coat closet. 'See you around six.'

'Don't forget Bobby's school,' she said.

Adams stopped, and looked at her. 'What about it?' he asked.

'They're having Father's Day,' she said. 'Remember?'

☛

'Oh, my God,' Adams said. He paused, then said hurriedly, 'I can't make it. It's out of the question.'

'You've got to,' she said. 'You missed it last year, and he was terribly hurt. Just go for a few minutes, but you've got to do it. I promised him I'd remind you.'

Adams drew a deep breath and said nothing.

'Bobby said you could just come for the English class,' Eleanor went on. 'Between twelve twenty and one. Please don't let him down again.'

Bobby's father does eventually go to the school, and finds the English classroom.

After hesitating a few seconds, Adams turned the knob and quietly opened the door. The first face he saw was that of his son, in the front row, and Bobby winked at him. Then Adams looked at the thin, dark-haired teacher, who seemed a surprisingly young man. He obviously had noticed Bobby's wink, and he smiled and said, 'Mr Adams.' Adams tiptoed to the back of the room and joined about six other fathers, who were sitting in various attitudes of discomfort on a row of folding chairs. He recognised none of them, but they look at him in a friendly way and he smiled at them, acknowledging the bond of uneasiness that held them momentarily together.

The teacher was diagramming a sentence on the blackboard, breaking it down into its component parts by means of straight and oblique lines, and Adams, looking at the diagram, realised that, if called upon, he would be hard put to it to separate the subject from the predicate, and he prayed that the teacher wouldn't suffer a fit of whimsy and call on the fathers. As it turned out, the students were well able to handle the problem, ☞

and Adams was gratified to hear his son give correct answers to two questions that were put to him. 'I'll be damned,' Adams thought. 'I never got the impression he knew all that.'

Then the problem was completed, and the teacher glanced at the clock and said, 'All right. Now we'll hear the compositions.' He walked to the back of the room, sat down, and then looked around at a field of suddenly upraised hands and said, 'Go ahead, Getsinger. You go first.'

A thin boy with wild blond hair and a red bow tie popped out of his seat and, carrying a sheet of paper, went to the front of the room and, in a fast, singsong voice, read. 'He's So Understanding. I like my Dad because he's so understanding.' Several of the boys turned in their seats and looked at one of the fathers and grinned as Getsinger went on, 'When I ask Dad for a dime he says he'll settle for a nickel, and I say you can't get anything for a nickel any more and he says then he'll settle for six cents. Then pretty soon Mom calls and says that supper is ready, and the fight goes on in the dining room, and after a while Dad says he'll make it seven cents, and before supper is over I have my dime. That's why I say he's understanding.'

Adams smiled in sympathy for Mr Getsinger and when the next boy got up and started off 'Why I Like My Father', Adams realised with horror that all the compositions were going to be on the same subject, and he saw that his own son had a piece of paper on his desk and was waiting eagerly for his turn to read. The palms of Adams' hands became moist, and he looked at the clock, hoping that the time would run out before Bobby got a chance to recite. There was a great deal of laughter during the second boy's reading of his composition, and after he sat down, Adams looked at the clock again and saw that there were seven minutes left. The the teacher looked around again, and five or six hands shot up, including Bobby's, and the teacher said, 'All ☞

right – let's have Satterlee next,' and Bobby took his hand down slowly, and Adams breathed more easily and kept his eyes rivetted on the clock.

Satterlee, goaded by the laughter the previous student had received, read his composition with a mincing attempt to be comical, and he told how his father was unable to get any peace around the house, with his mother 'chattering about the latest gossip' and his sister practising the violin. It occurred to Adams that the compositions were nothing more than the children's impressions of their own home life, and the squirming and the nervous laughter from the fathers indicated that the observations were more acute than flattering. Adams tried to think what Bobby might say, and he could remember only things like the time he had docked Bobby's allowance for two weeks, for some offence he couldn't now recall, and the way he sometimes shouted at Bobby when he got too boisterous around the apartment, and the time Bobby had threatened to leave home because he had been forbidden to go to a vaudeville show – and the time he *had* left home because of a punishment Adams had given him. Adams thought also of the night he and his wife had had an argument, and how, the next day, Bobby had asked what 'self-centred' meant, in reply to which Adams had told him it was none of his business. Then he remembered the time Bobby had been on a children's radio show and had announced that his household chores included getting out the ice for drinks, and when Adams asked him later why he had said it, Bobby had reminded him of one time Adams had asked him to bring an ice tray from the pantry into the living room. The memories they have, Adams thought – the diabolically selective memories.

Satterlee finished. The clock showed two minutes to one, and Adams wiped his hands on his trouser legs and gripped his hat, which was getting pulpy around the brim. Then Bobby's hand ☞

went up again, almost plaintively now, and the teacher said, 'All right, Adams, you're on,' and Bobby bobbed up and went to the front of the room.

Several of the boys turned and looked at Adams as Bobby began to read, but Adams was oblivious of everything except the stocky figure in front of the blackboard, whose tweed jacket looked too small for him and who was reading fast because the bell was about to ring. What Bobby read was a list of things that Adams had completely forgotten, or that had seemed of no great importance at the time, things like being allowed to stay up late to watch a fight, and being given an old fencing mask when there was no occasion for a gift (Adams had simply found it in a secondhand store and thought Bobby might like it), and having a model airplane made for him when he couldn't do it himself, and the time Adams had retrieved the ring from the subway grating. By the time Bobby concluded with 'That's why he's OK in *my* book', Adams had recovered from his surprise and was beginning to feel embarrassed. Then the bell rang and class was dismissed, and Adams and the other fathers followed the boys out of the room.

Bobby was waiting for him in the corridor outside.

'Hi,' Bobby said. 'You going now?'

'Yes,' said Adams. 'I'm afraid I've got to.'

'OK,' Bobby turned and started away.

'Just a minute,' Adams said, and Bobby stopped and looked back. Adams walked over to him and then hesitated a moment. 'That was – ah – a good speech,' he said.

'Thanks,' said Bobby.

Adams started to say something else, but could think of nothing. 'See you later,' he finished, and quickly put on his hat and hurried down the stairs. ◆

NATHANIEL BENCHLEY

19

The Eve of Ramadan

Because the Muslim year is shorter than the Western year, the annual events in the Muslim calendar occur at different times in the Western one. So, for example, the month of Ramadan is 'earlier' each year. Ramadan is the month in which Muslims fast each day during daylight hours. This passage describes what it is like in a Middle Eastern city on the last Friday or Holy Day before the start of the month of Ramadan.

(Note: The word imsak *means the period of fasting;* iftar *means literally breakfast, or the breaking of the fast each evening once it is dark;* adhan *is the call to prayer.)*

What is the longest period you have gone without food? Imagine what it is like to go without anything to eat for twelve hours or more each day for a month! This is what members of the Muslim religion do each day during their month of Ramadan. That is, they neither eat nor drink anything from the moment there is any daylight at all until after sunset each evening. In our reading today we hear what it is like in a city in the Middle East on the last day before the start of the month of Ramadan when people are preparing for the period of fasting.

◆

THIS IS THE last Friday before Ramadan, and most Muslim householders will spend today preparing for the Holy Month, buying the things they would need for *imsak* and *iftar*. There is already a sense of subdued excitement in the air, because Ramadan is not merely a religious occasion: it is part of a social set-up when the pace of Gulf life changes and briefly assumes a new pattern.

Offices close early, and by the afternoon the roads begin to ☞

wear a deserted look. The shops are shuttered and taxi-drivers idly patrol the streets looking in vain for passengers.

But as the long afternoon draws to an end and the shadows begin to lengthen, the city slowly comes back to life in a way it does only during Ramadan. The shops reopen, one by one, and people begin to come out of the houses to buy spicy knick-knacks or pick up some crisp, fresh lettuce for the evening meal. Children come out to play again, but keep an ear glued to hear the *adhan* which will announce the end of the fast, when they will scamper inside to have a glass of cold milk or sherbet.

The street-side vendors appear around *iftar* time and arrange their tempting wares in neat rows. A little oil is poured into the frying pan and it begins to simmer, ready for the *samosas* to be put in. Dates are heaped in little mounds and find ready customers because traditionally this desert fruit is used to break the fast.

Then, the cannon booms out to announce *iftar* and from countless minarets rises the call of the muezzin. Another day's duty has been fulfilled, and the faithful are free to eat and drink till sunrise.

Even after the night prayers, there is much activity everywhere as people sit outside their houses and the children play football in the sand. Some people go to the few old-style open-air coffee houses still in existence, sit on the wooden benches and exchange the news and recall past Ramadans, when sharing and kinship went beyond one's immediate family. Then, Ramadan embraced the entire community and the better-off would maintain open-house throughout the month, with the Holy Quran being recited during the night and the gathering continuing till *imsak*.

Much of that has changed, but Ramadan still draws the family ☞

together and there is still that alternation between self-denial and rejoicing that lends the month its essential charm. ◆

KHALEEJ TIMES

20

To Everything There Is a Season . . .

*These two short passages are offered for use at various times throughout
the year when a particular mood seems to strike the school. For example,
they might either or both be used at a time of sadness or tension. They
might also be used at the end of a school year or at an assembly for leavers.
According to use, they will require their own topical introductions.*

To everything there is a season, and a time to every purpose
under the heaven.

A time to be born and a time to die; a time to plant and a
time to pluck up that which is planted.

A time to kill and a time to heal; a time to break down and a
time to build up.

A time to weep and a time to laugh; a time to mourn and a
time to dance.

A time to get and a time to lose; a time to keep and a time to
cast away.

A time to rend and a time to sew; a time to keep silence and
a time to speak.

That which hath been, is now; and that which is to be hath
already been; and God requireth that which is past.

All go unto one place; all are of the dust, and all turn to dust
again.

Wherefore I perceive that there is nothing better than that a
man should rejoice in his own works; for that is his
portion; for who shall bring him to see what shall be after
him?

ECCLESIASTES 1.9; 3.1–8, 15, 20, 22

AUTHORISED VERSION

Take time to work –
it is the price of success.
Take time to think –
it is the source of power.
Take time to play –
it is the secret of perpetual youth.
Take time to read –
it is the foundation of wisdom.
Take time to be friendly –
it is the road to happiness.
Take time to dream –
it is hitching your wagon to a star.
Take time to love and be loved –
it is the privilege of the Gods.
Take time to look around –
the day is too short to be selfish.
Take time to laugh –
it is the music of the soul. ◆

AN OLD IRISH PRAYER

STORIES, PARABLES AND LEGENDS

Someone said to an Eastern mystic:
'You relate stories, but you do not tell us how to understand
them.'
He said:
'How would you like it if the man from whom you bought fruit
consumed it before your eyes, leaving only the skin?'

IDRIES SHAH

21

The Creation

Most cultures have their own creation myths and legends. This poetic reworking of the Genesis story emphasises the religious belief that there is a divine Being who initiated the creation, but circumvents some of the more literal details of the story as told in the first book of the Bible. It is offered here as a reading to illustrate the Christian belief in the greatness and glory of God.

How did the world begin? With a big bang? And, if so, what existed before that explosion? People who believe in God say that God has always existed and that he created the world and space as we know it. Many people have tried to find ways of explaining this in stories and poetry. This is one version of the creation story.

◆

(Except for non-commercial use in schools, no readings can be done without first obtaining permission from Penguin USA).

And God stepped out on space,
And he looked around and said:
I'm lonely –
I'll make me a world.

As far as the eye of God could see
Darkness covered everything,
Blacker than a hundred midnights
Down in a cypress swamp.

Then God smiled,
And the light broke,
And the darkness rolled up on one side,

And the light stood shining on the other,
And God said: That's good!

Then God reached out and took the light in his hands,
And God rolled the light around in his hands
Until he made the sun;
And he set that sun a-blazing in the heavens.
And the light that was left from making the sun
God gathered it up in a shining ball
And flung it against the darkness,
Spangling the night with the moon and stars.
Then down between
The darkness and the light
He hurled the world;
And God said: That's good!

Then God himself stepped down –
And the sun was on his right hand,
And the moon was on his left;
The stars were clustered about his head,
And the earth was under his feet.
And God walked, and where he trod
His footsteps hollowed the valleys out
And bulged the mountains up.

Then he stopped and looked and saw
That the earth was hot and barren.
So God stepped over to the edge of the world
And he spat out the seven seas –
He batted his eyes, and the lightnings flashed –
He clapped his hands, and the thunders rolled –
And the waters above the earth came down,
The cooling waters came down.

Then the green grass sprouted,

And the little red flowers blossomed,
The pine tree pointed his finger to the sky,
And the oak spread out his arms,
The lakes cuddled down in the hollows of the ground,
And the rivers ran down to the sea;
And God smiled again,
And the rainbow appeared
And curled itself around his shoulder.

Then God raised his arm and he waved his hand
Over the sea and over the land,
And he said: Bring forth! Bring forth!
And quicker than God could drop his hand,
Fishes and fowls
And beasts and birds
Swam the rivers and the seas,
Roamed the forests and the woods,
And split the air with their wings.
And God said: That's good!

Then God walked around,
And God looked around
On all that he had made.
He looked at his sun,
And he looked at his moon,
And he looked at his little stars;
He looked on his world
With all its living things,
And God said: I'm lonely still.

Then God sat down –
On the side of a hill where he could think;
By a deep, wide river he sat down;
With his head in his hands,

God thought and thought,
Till he thought, I'll make me a man!
Up from the bed of the river
God scooped the clay;
And by the bank of the river
He kneeled him down;
And there the great God Almighty
Who lit the sun and fixed it in the sky,
Who flung the stars to the most far corner of the night,
Who rounded the earth in the middle of hand;
This great God,
Like a mammy bending over her baby,
Kneeled down in the dust
Toiling over a lump of clay
Till he shaped it in his own image;
Then into it he blew the breath of life,
And man became a living soul.
Amen. Amen. ◆

JAMES WELDON JOHNSON

22

King Midas

Midas was a semi-legendary king of Phrygia. When he had entertained a friend of the god Bacchus (also known as Dionysus) who had lost his way, the god was so pleased that Midas was allowed to choose a reward. This legend is a permanent warning against the dangers of greed!

Today's reading is an ancient legend about a Greek called Midas who, although a king, was still a very greedy man. You can probably decide for yourself what is the moral of this story!

◆

THOUSANDS OF YEARS ago, there was a king called Midas. Midas did something that greatly pleased Bacchus, the god of Revelry, and so Bacchus told him that he could choose for himself any present that he liked. 'You have only to ask and your wish will be granted,' Bacchus said.

Of course, Midas was pleased, but the wonderful chance he had been given did him little good, for he made a stupid mistake. 'I wish that anything I touch shall be turned into gold,' he asked the god. Bacchus frowned, for he thought that Midas ought to have asked for something a little less ambitious. But, he granted the king's request.

At first, Midas was as happy as he could have been, for everything that he touched turned instantly into gold – he plucked a twig from an oak tree and the twig and the leaves on it immediately became gold; he picked up a stone, and the stone at once became a lump of precious metal; he touched a clod of earth, and the clod became a gleaming nugget. He was able to turn corn and fruit into gold by the power of his touch. ☞

Soon, he had turned the whole of his palace into gold, and every stick of furniture that the palace contained.

Overjoyed by his unexpected good fortune and seeing that there was nothing to stop him becoming the richest man, by far, in the whole of the known world, Midas decided to hold a great feast. Obediently, his servants prepared a magnificent banquet, loading the king's tables with delicious foods of many different kinds and with wines of the very best vintages. But the king was to be bitterly disappointed. Every time he tried to sink his teeth into an appetising piece of food, the food turned into gold. The wine, too, turned into gold as soon as it touched the king's lips. He could swallow nothing.

Realising that he would soon starve to death or die in agony, of thirst, and shocked by the dreadful fate that he had brought on himself, Midas prayed desperately to Bacchus for relief. 'Forgive me, Father Bacchus,' he implored the god. 'I have done wrong, I know, and I deserve to be punished, but do not destroy me utterly, I beseech you!'

Seeing that Midas had learned his lesson and was sorry for his greedy actions, Bacchus decided to take away from him the power of turning other materials into gold. 'Now go and dip yourself in the river that runs by the great city of Sardis,' he told Midas. 'Bathe yourself where the water rises, and all will be well.'

Midas did as he was told, and the strange power that Bacchus had given him passed into the foaming spring. From that time on, the waters of the river that flowed from the spring were the colour of gold, and Midas was able to lead a more or less normal life again. ◆

OVID
adapted by Guy Williams

23

Axe Porridge

This traditional Russian story is offered as an exercise in moral education. Is the soldier in the story justified in his action?

Today you're going to hear an ancient story from Russia. It's about an old soldier and you have to decide whether the trick he plays in the story is fair or mean.

◆

AN OLD SOLDIER was once on his way home for his leave, and he was tired and hungry. He reached a village and he rapped at the first hut.

'Let a traveller in for the night,' said he.

The door was opened by an old woman.

'Come in, soldier,' she offered.

'Have you a bite of food for a hungry man, good dame?' the soldier asked.

Now the old woman had plenty of everything, but she was stingy and pretended to be very poor.

'Ah, me, I've had nothing to eat myself today, dear heart, there is nothing in the house,' she wailed.

'Well, if you've nothing, you've nothing,' the soldier said. Then, noticing an axe without a handle under the bench: 'If there's nothing else, we could make porridge out of that axe.'

The old woman raised both hands in astonishment.

'Axe porridge? Who ever heard the like!'

'I'll show you how to make it. Just give me a pot.'

The old woman brought a pot, and the soldier washed the axe, put it in the pot and, filling the pot with water, placed it on the fire.

The soldier got out a spoon and stirred the water and then tasted it.

'It will soon be ready,' said he. 'A pity there's no salt.'

'Oh, I have salt. Here, take some.'

The soldier put some salt in the pot and then tried the water again.

'If we could just add a handful of oats to it,' said he.

The old woman brought a small bag of oats from the pantry.

'Here, add as much as you need,' said she.

The soldier went on with his cooking, stirring the meal from time to time and tasting it. And the old woman watched, and could not tear her eyes away.

'Oh, how tasty this porridge is!' the soldier said, trying a spoonful. 'With a bit of butter there would be nothing more delicious.'

The old woman found some butter too, and they buttered the porridge.

'Now get a spoon, good dame, and let us eat!' the soldier said.

They began eating the porridge and praising it.

'I never thought axe porridge could taste so good!' the old woman marvelled.

And the soldier ate, and laughed up his sleeve. ◆

TRADITIONAL

24

The Dreamer and the Treasure

This Icelandic folk tale is an example of a little-known but impressive tradition of oral story telling. This and many other similar Icelandic tales reflect the longings, fears and beliefs of the Icelandic people – together with their characteristic sense of humour. This story is one of several that demonstrate a belief that our souls can 'wander' on their own. It raises a number of questions, such as to what extent we should believe our dreams (or 'hunches') – and even act upon them. The story might also be useful for inculcating a sense of the mysterious.

Do you believe that we can learn things from our dreams? If you had a dream that suggested that you should do something, would you be prepared to act upon it (provided it did not cause you to get into any danger)? This story comes from Iceland and was first told many years ago.

◆

A GOOD MANY men were once travelling together, and one Sunday morning they pitched tent on a pleasant grassy field; the weather was clear and bright. These men all lay down to sleep, lying in a row in the tent. The one nearest the entrance could not get to sleep, so he was looking at one thing or another in the tent. Then he saw a wisp of bluish vapour hovering above the man who lay furthest in, and then this wisp drifted through the tent and out into the open.

The man wanted to know what this could be, so he followed the vapour. It drifted gently, very gently, across the field, and finally came to where an old horse-hide and skull were lying; these were full of blowflies, and they were buzzing loudly. The vapour drifted inside the horse skull. A good while later, it ☞

came out again and drifted off across the field once more, till it came to a tiny brook which ran through the field. It followed the course of this downstream, and it looked to the man as if it was trying to cross. The man was carrying a whip, and this he laid right across the brook (for it was so narrow that the handle could reach right across), and the wisp of vapour went along the handle of the whip and so drifted across the brook. Then it went on again, and eventually reached a little tussock in the field. The vapour vanished down inside this. The man stood and waited for it to come back. Soon it came. Then it went back again along the same track as it had come; the man laid his whip across the brook and the vapour crossed along it as before, and then it went straight home to the tent, never stopping till it was hovering over the man who lay furthest in, and then it disappeared. Then the other man lay down and fell asleep.

Towards evening the travellers got up and fetched their horses, and as they were busy loading them up, they chatted of this and that, and among other things the man who had been sleeping at the inner end of the tent said: 'I wish I owned what I was dreaming of today.'

'What was it? What did you dream of?' says the one who had seen the vapour.

The other says: 'I thought I was walking about out here on this field. Then I came to a splendid large house where a crowd had gathered and were singing and playing with the greatest merriment and glee, and I stayed a long time in that house. When I came out again, I walked a long, long way across fine level plains, until I came to a broad river which I tried for a long time to cross, but I could not. Then I saw a terrifyingly huge giant coming; he was carrying an enormous big tree in his hand which he laid across the river, and so I crossed it by the way of the tree.

'Then I walked on again for a long, long way, till I came to a huge burial mound. It was open, and I went in, and what did I find there but a great barrel, full of money! I stayed an immensely long time in there, staring at the money, for I had never seen such a heap as that before. Then I came out again and went home by the same way as I had come, and when I reached the river the same giant came with his tree and laid it across, so that I crossed by way of the tree, and so came home again to the tent.'

The man who had tracked the vapour was filled with secret glee, and says to the one who had had this dream: 'Come along, my friend, let's go and look for that money at once.'

The other burst out laughing, thinking that he wasn't quite right in the head, but all the same he did go. They follow the route which the vapour had taken, come to the tussock, and dig it up, and there they find a keg full of money. Then they went back to their companions, told them the whole story of the dream and vapour, and showed them the keg of treasure. ◆

JACQUELINE SIMPSON

25

The Most Precious Merchandise

This Jewish story, taken from Jewish holy writings, emphasises the importance to believers of Holy Scripture.

This is a story told by Jewish people about a merchant who went on a journey. It teaches one simple lesson, which should be quite obvious by the end of the story.

◆

A LONG, LONG time ago, a great sailing ship was getting ready to leave port for a distant country. Going on board were many wealthy merchants, while all the valuable things they hoped to sell in that country were being loaded into the ship's hold, down below deck. There were clothes made of finest silk, jewels, gold and silver and many, many cases of expensive wine.

Among the passengers on the ship was a stranger; a man the other merchants did not know.

'And what do you trade in?' they asked. 'What merchandise do you bring?'

'The most precious in the world.'

'What is that?' they all asked. But he'd say nothing more.

So they went below deck to see if they could discover what he'd brought on board. They checked every package and every packing case, but all they could find were their own cases. When they realised the stranger had no baggage at all, they began to laugh among themselves. 'He's not a merchant. He's brought nothing to sell.'

Soon they set sail. After several days at sea, a great storm arose and the ship was badly damaged. The sails were torn to ribbons, the mast broken, and soon they were drifting helplessly towards some jagged rocks. There was nothing they could do to prevent the shipwreck. With a great crash the wind drove the ship on to the rocks; and there it stuck fast. The passengers and crew were able to scramble ashore, but the wind and waves attacked what remained of the ship. Soon its timbers were beaten to splinters and all the cargo was lost, washed back out to sea.

As it turned out, they had reached the country to which they had been sailing and were able to make their way on foot to the city where they had hoped to sell their goods. But instead of becoming rich, the merchants had to beg. Beg for food and beg for somewhere to sleep. But the stranger among them, well, he went to the local synagogue and asked to teach the congregation. What he said showed he was a very learned man – and indeed he had spent his whole life studying the Torah, the five books of Moses.

The people of the synagogue were greatly honoured to have such a person among them and asked him to stay with them. They also asked him to teach regularly in the synagogue and paid him to teach in a local academy or college. Many people came to listen to him as he explained the Torah. After several weeks, though, the time came for him to return home. The people were sad to see him go, but they gave him many presents.

When the merchants heard of all this they were astonished and came and asked if he could help them to return to their home country.

The teacher told the people of the synagogue what the merchants wanted. The people said they would pay for the ☛

merchants to travel home on the same ship as the teacher – because such a learned man had asked on their behalf.

And so the merchants and the teacher all went on board ship together – and as they put out to sea, the teacher said to the merchants, 'You thought I brought nothing with me. No merchandise. But I did. I brought something really valuable. I brought *knowledge.* The knowledge and teaching of the Torah. That is something more precious than any jewels or silver or gold.'

And the merchants were silent because they knew now that this was so.

'Rabbi,' said one of them, 'you speak true. Yours *is* the most precious merchandise.' ◆

26

Chopsticks

No apology is made for including this well-known story in this anthology of readings. Its simple message – that we can achieve more by co-operation than by fighting one another – is straightforward and indeed obvious. That does not mean that we do not have to teach this lesson from time to time! Although some children may have come across the story before, there will always be new generations to whom its message can make a direct appeal.

(Note: It may be used effectively in conjunction with charity fund-raising events.)

You may just have been in a Chinese restaurant and seen people eating with chopsticks. You may even have tried using them yourself. At first, it's not easy. But think how much more difficult it would be if the chopsticks were longer than your arms! This is a story they tell in an eastern country called Korea – and it has a message for us, whether we use chopsticks or not.

◆

IN KOREA THERE is a legend about a native warrior who died and went to heaven. 'Before I enter,' he said to the gate-keeper, 'I would like you to take me on a tour of hell.' The gate-keeper found a guide to take the warrior to hell. When he got there he was astonished to see a great table piled high with the choicest of foods. But the people in hell were starving. The warrior turned to his guide and raised his eyebrows.

'It's this way,' the guide explained. 'Everybody who comes here is given a pair of chopsticks five feet long, and is required to hold them at the end to eat. But you just can't eat with ☞

chopsticks five feet long if you hold them at the end. Look at them. They miss their mouths every time, see?'

The visitor agreed that this was hell indeed and asked to be taken back to heaven post-haste. In heaven, to his surprise, he saw a similar room with a similar table laden with very choice foods. But the people were happy, they looked radiantly happy.

The visitor turned to the guide. 'No chopsticks, I suppose?' he said.

'O yes,' said the guide, 'they have the same chopsticks, the same length, and they must be held at the end just as in hell. But you see, these people have learned that if a man feeds his neighbour, his neighbour will feed him also.' ◆

JOHN P. HOGAN

27

The Serpent King

For many Hindus, the god Vishnu is the centre of their faith. Whenever evil has threatened to triumph over good, Vishnu has come to the aid of human beings.

Most Hindus recognise ten 'avatars' or incarnations of the god Vishnu. The eighth avatar of Vishnu and one of Hinduism's most widely worshipped gods is Krishna. He was born of royal blood, but grew up in the countryside among farm workers. Even as a boy, Krishna killed many demons – as this passage illustrates. The story may be used as an example of the way in which believers, whichever world faith they follow, trust that God will answer their prayers.

Jesus once told his followers, 'Ask and ye shall receive.' That is, if you ask God to help you, then (in his own way) he will. It may not always be in the way in which we expect or hope to receive help, but even so he will help us. This Hindu story shows how the god Krishna, even when he was young, helped *his* followers.

◆

KALIYA, THE SERPENT King was no ordinary snake. He had five heads and was so large that he could crush humans to death in a matter of seconds. The Serpent King lived under the darkest whirlpools of the Yamuna River and this is where he held his court.

Whenever he so wished, he would rise out of the water and lay waste the countryside, ferociously breathing fire and black smoke wherever he went.

Krishna was almost twelve years old by now. Even at this tender age he was the acknowledged leader among his friends ☛

and looked upon with great respect by the large community of nomadic cowherds that moved wherever the pasture was good.

One day, a group of cowherds came to Krishna and said, 'Kaliya must be stopped. He has already swallowed three hundred chickens, a hundred and seventy-eight goats, and eighty-three cows. Yesterday he killed the blacksmith's son. This is the last straw. Anyone that tries to cross the river, swim, graze cattle, grow watermelons, milk goats or even walk by the river is in danger. Something must be done.'

Krishna collected a group of brave friends and walked towards the edge of the water. Suddenly a cloud of black smoke rose above the river, shooting flames swirled upwards and, in one quick swipe, Kaliya encircled all of Krishna's friends in the curl of his body and dragged them down to the bottom of the river.

Having done their dirty deed, the five dreaded heads bobbed up again, breaking the surface of the water. This time the Serpent King was floating along casually, mockingly.

Krishna took one flying leap and landed on all the five hooded heads of the dreaded snake. He crushed one head under one arm and another head under another arm. With his feet he began a heavy-footed dance on the remaining three.

Kaliya felt as if all the mountains of the Himalayas were raining on his head. Such was the power of Krishna's feet.

He decided to dive into his under-water court. He would drown Krishna this way.

Krishna held his breath as Kaliya dived deeper and deeper.

Having killed two of Kaliya's heads Krishna began squeezing ☛

the next two under his arms until they also gave up and died.

The last head fought on. It snapped and lunged at Krishna and breathed fire on him, but Krishna trapped that head, too, under his arm and began to squeeze.

Kaliya gave a few last gasps and died.

Krishna swam into Kaliya's court where all his friends, now quite pale and blue, lay dying. He pulled them out of the water and laid them down on the shore. Then, with his mouth, he breathed life into each one saying, 'Dearest friends, it is time to awaken. Kaliya our enemy is dead. Awaken. Awaken. It is time to tend our cows.' ◆

MADHUR JAFFREY

28

Saints and Sinners

The Jewish actor-writer David Kossoff has written a series of portraits of characters who appear in the Bible, including this one of the woman taken in adultery. Each portrait is narrated by a different character. Here, David Kossoff describes this woman through the eyes of a beggar whom he nicknames 'Kwuz'. Kossoff suggests that Kwuz is an oldish man, with piercing hard eyes and a thin, cruel mouth. He is a beggar.

The story of the woman taken in adultery can be found in the opening verses of the eighth chapter of John's Gospel. It is one of the relatively few occasions in the New Testament from which we can deduce Jesus' views on sexual morality. Sometimes it has been taken as a support for sexual permissiveness. However, the last words of Jesus to the woman are 'Sin no more.' (See also passage No. 35.)

This is a story about Jesus, told not by one of his followers, but by a Jewish beggar who observed this particular incident in the life of Jesus. It shows how Jesus forgave people who had done wrong, but it also shows how Jesus taught that we should always try to do what is right.

◆

ONE TIME IN particular. I think of that occasion a lot. When Jesus of Galilee sat as near to me as you are. Just the once, I remember it like yesterday – and it's nearly eleven years. It's about nine or ten since he died. Nasty business. He was a remarkable man, the Carpenter, in many ways. I always felt a sort of kinship with him. We had things in common. No money, no possessions – and we weren't fooled by people. I know he loved 'em all and I hate 'em all, but we *knew* about them, they didn't fool us. I've sat on this stone seat, in this corner near the gate of this part of the Temple for nearly fifty ☞

years. I've seen it all. If I tell you that most people are not worth twopence, it's not because I've got no legs and I'm all twisted, it's because I've been observing people all my life. All day every day. I can't write a letter, or read a book, so I sit and watch the whole stupid comedy. The way people rush about and hurt each other and think they're clever. The way people seem to think that no one knows what they're up to. The beggars know it all.

We beggars have the most accurate and the fastest news grapevine in Israel. We know everything. I knew about the Carpenter being baptised by his cousin John the day after it happened. The wedding at Cana with the water-into-wine business, the loaves and fishes, the healing of the sick, the disturbance he made here in the Temple with the money changers, how they threw him out of the synagogue in Nazareth, everything. I could have told you the exact day that the authorities decided to put a stop to him. From that day he was a marked man. They were at every meeting, in every crowd. Experts in the Law, high priests, the 'Establishment'. But he could handle them. As I said, one day he sat here next to me. In the open. Talking to a huge crowd. Teaching, making it simple. Suddenly a gang of Pharisees and lawyers pushed their way through, dragging a woman. I knew her. A man had left his wife for her. Not unknown, such behaviour. Plenty of it went on. The Pharisees, a holier-than-thou lot, were there to make the Carpenter look a fool. Or to make him say something that they could hang a charge on. They pushed the woman forward and made a half-ring round her.

'An adulteress!' they screamed. 'Proven! Great Moses said such women must be stoned to death. What do *you* say?'

The crowd were silent. Some of them edged forward, looking ☞

for stones. Very little difference between a crowd and a mob, you know. The woman and Jesus looked at each other. Then the Carpenter sat forward and reached down and wrote something in the dust by his feet and his finger. His head down. He didn't hurry. The Pharisees and lawyers screamed for him to answer. He got up and it went very quiet. Then he said, 'Yes, she sinned. Let the first stone be thrown by the one among you who has never sinned.' Then he looked at the crowd, and they went as still as he was. After a moment or two he sat down again, very calm, and again he bent down and wrote with his finger in the dust. As near to me as you are. Very quiet.

The people began to shuffle and the eldest of the party who'd brought the woman walked away. Then another. Then another. Soon she was by herself. Jesus lifted his head from the finger-writing and looked at the woman.

'All by yourself?' he said. 'Everybody gone? No stoning? No sentence? Did no one condemn you?'

'No one,' she said. She was crying. I wasn't surprised. Jesus got up and went to her.

'And I don't condemn you either,' he said. 'Go home and don't do it again.'

She went out by that gate, and the crowd moved forward to surround the Carpenter, to be near to him. Soon the writing in the dust was gone. And, because I can't read, I shall never know what it said. ◆

DAVID KOSSOFF

29

Faith, Hope *and* Charity
(The Good Samaritan)

The parable of the Good Samaritan is one of the best known stories that Jesus told. It can be found in Luke 10.30–37 and was told by Jesus to answer a lawyer's question, 'Who is my neighbour?'

It is a useful exercise to try to find ways of retelling the parable in modern terms. Which two modern, apparently 'holy', characters might ignore someone in need and which unattractive reprobate might actually come to the aid of someone who has been injured and left by the roadside? (In the original story, the injured traveller is ignored by a priest and a temple official, known as a Levite. The Samaritan who came to his aid was a person of mixed race and therefore disdained by many Jews of that period.)

This is a translation from a Middle English retelling of the parable.

In the Bible it tells us to 'love our neighbours'. But who are our 'neighbours'? They are not just the people who live next door. When Jesus was asked this question he told the story that has become known as the Parable of the Good Samaritan. This is a retelling of that story from a different point of view. In order to understand it you must remember that, in Jesus' time, Samaritans were looked down upon as people of mixed race and therefore, sad though it may seem, the friends of no one. By the end of the story you can perhaps work out the moral it is teaching us.

◆

I WALKED THE road, deep in conversation
With the two men. One was talking of faith,
The other of hope. Suddenly we saw
A Samaritan on a mule, moving
At speed in the same direction as us.
He came on the Jericho road, making
For the tournament in Jerusalem.
Together the four of us came upon
A man lying injured. Thieves had beaten
Him up and left him for dead. He couldn't
Take a step, stand up, even stir a foot
Or flex his hands. There was nothing he could
Do for himself. He seemed to be half dead,
Stripped naked as a needle, nobody
There to help him. The man who talked about
Faith had noticed him first but slipped quickly
By and wouldn't touch him with a bargepole.
The one who'd been on about hope tiptoed
Along next. He'd just been bragging about
All the people he'd helped by following
What the ten commandments said you should do.
And then he saw the man and took off past
Him, God help us! really scared, like a duck
Cringing from a falcon. But as soon as
The Samaritan saw the body there,
He dismounted and, leading his mule, went
To the man to inspect his wounds. He felt
His pulse, realised he was not far off
Dying and if he didn't get fixed up,
That was it, he'd never get up again.
So he unstrapped his bottles, opened them
Both and bathed the man's wounds with wine and oil,
Smeared him with healing ointments and bandaged

His head. Then picking him up in his arms
He put him across his mule and took him
To the farming village they call Christlaw
Six miles or so from the new market town.
He made him comfortable at the inn, called
The landlord and said, 'Look after this man
Till I get back from the tournament. Here's
The money to keep his wounds dressed.' He gave
Him enough for the expenses and said,
'If you need more I'll pay the bill later.
Now I must get on.' The Samaritan
Remounted his mule and then galloped out
At great speed on the Jerusalem road. ◆

WILLIAM LANGLAND
translated by Ronald Tamplin

30

The Wealthy Man

This parable attempts to give an explanation (from a Christian point of view) of the relationship between God and the people he has created. It is not an exact parallel and it may therefore be fruitful to discuss which parts are most 'satisfactory', or to discuss whether this is a fair way for a father to behave towards his children. For example, would we like our own parents (or God) to interfere more in our lives?

(Note: It may be a good idea to read the story to a group twice, once before giving any clue as to its metaphorical meaning; and then a second time, after pointing out the intended parallel.)

This is another story with a 'meaning'. On one level it seems to be simply a story about a wealthy man and how he treated his children – but you might care to remember that Christians often call God their Father in heaven and think of themselves as his children . . .

◆

A WEALTHY MAN had a large number of children, but their mother died. As he had to go abroad for long periods on business, he made careful plans for their care and education. He took a large house by the seaside, hired nurses, cooks, gardener and tutors, and settled his children in their new home, together with a number of cousins and friends as well. He had ponies for the children to ride, but chose only safe, docile beasts. He had barbed wire put at the top of the cliffs, and saw to it that every danger was removed. He instructed his staff to watch over the children day and night, and take great care of them. Then he went on his long journey.

Three years passed, and the father returned. It was a happy ☞

reunion. All the children were well, and they had all grown taller. There had been no serious illnesses or accidents, and they had made steady progress with their schooling. At the same time, the father felt there was something lacking; the children were too docile and listless. He soon decided what was wrong. He gave all the staff a month's notice, and told the children that after that they would have to look after themselves. There would be food for a year, but they would have to cook it themselves; and there would be no food after that unless they grew it themselves. He replaced their ponies with some more spirited ones, and had the barbed wire and other safeguards removed. Then he went off again on his journeys.

At first the children thought it was great fun to have no nursemaids or tutors to tell them what to do. They could eat what they liked, when they liked, and they could do what they liked. Soon, however, they found it was not so funny. None of them was much good at cooking and sometimes they were very ill. They were not much good at farming, and in the second year they nearly starved. One boy fell from a tree and broke his arm; one girl was thrown from her horse and broke her leg; one boy fell over the cliff and was killed. When their father returned at the end of the third year they had all suffered a great deal. He was grieved to hear of the tragedy and to find that they had met so much trouble; but when he saw his children he was pleased to see that they were alert, wiser and more mature. They had grown inwardly as well as in physical stature. He felt that he had made the right decision. ◆

ANON.

31

Footprints

This well-known modern parable teaches the Christian belief that 'the Lord' (i.e. God or Jesus) is caring for us at all times, whether we realise it or not.

Christians believe that God cares for them at all times in ways they do not always notice. This is a story that illustrates this belief.

◆

ONE NIGHT A man had a dream. He dreamed he was walking along the beach with the Lord. Across the sky flashed scenes from his life. For each scene, he noticed two sets of footprints in the sand: one belonging to him, and the other to the Lord.

When the last scene of his life flashed before him, he looked back at the footprints in the sand. He noticed that many times along the path of his life there was only one set of footprints. He also noticed that it happened at the very lowest and saddest times in his life.

This really bothered him and he questioned the Lord about it.

'Lord, you said that once I decided to follow you, you'd walk with me all the way. But I have noticed that during the most troublesome times in my life, there is only one set of footprints. I don't understand why, when I needed you most, you would leave me.'

The Lord replied, 'My son, my precious child, I love you and would never leave you. During your times of trial and suffering, when you see only one set of footprints, it was then that I carried you.' ◆

ANON.

32

The Night Journey

This happening is also known as the 'Miraj'. The story tells how Muhammad, the prophet of Islam, was taken from Makka to the Temple in Jerusalem, guided by the Archangel Gabriel and on a winged horse called Burraq. From the site where Solomon's Temple once stood, Muhammad made a journey into heaven, meeting several of the prophets on his way. On his return he was filled with God's message, which he preached to his followers. Besides being an important story within the religion of Islam, the Miraj points to many of the connections between three of the great world religions.

This story is about the prophet Muhammad, the founder of the religion of Islam. One night he felt himself taken on a strange journey from Makka, the holy city where he lived in what is now Saudi Arabia, to Jerusalem. From Jerusalem he felt himself guided into the presence of God in heaven. As you will hear, he met the leaders and teachers of other religions on his journey. This story shows us many things – for example, why the city of Jerusalem is holy not only to Jews and Christians, but also to Muslims. It also shows how the prophet Muhammad received several of the teachings of Islam which are still kept today by those who follow that religion.

◆

IT WAS NIGHT time in the holy city of Makka. The prophet Muhammad, tired after the heat and cares and general busyness of the day, slept deeply; quiet, untroubled sleep.

Then, suddenly, he heard a voice calling him – and he saw (standing by where he slept) the angel Gabriel. Gabriel was beckoning, beckoning the prophet Muhammad to follow him. ☛

Muhammad left his bed and followed the angel, across the room and out through the doorway of the house. And there, waiting for them, was the most magnificent white horse. A mare, with a flowing white mane. But, even more remarkable, the horse had wings like those of an eagle – but even larger.

'This is Burraq,' said Gabriel. Together they mounted Burraq and immediately the horse was flying, flying higher and higher through the cool night air – and the city of Makka was left far behind.

Before long, Gabriel told Burraq to descend from the night sky, back to earth – and as she did, Muhammad saw that they had arrived at another holy city, the city of Jerusalem. In just a short while, they had completed a journey that would have taken many days or even weeks had they travelled by land.

Burraq landed gently at the Temple that was in that city, and Muhammad tied the horse to a ring on the wall, as was the custom in those days. And then Gabriel led Muhammad into the Temple and there they met Moses and Jesus and holy men from other times – and they prayed there together.

Then, on leaving the Temple, Gabriel offered Muhammad a drink. A drink of either milk or wine. Muhammad chose milk. 'You have chosen rightly,' said Gabriel. 'From now on, Muslim people will not drink alcohol lest they go astray and do wrong.'

It was then that Muhammad saw another wondrous thing: a ladder, seemingly made out of light, leading up into heaven. And Gabriel signed to Muhammad that they should climb the ladder, and in this way Muhammad entered heaven. There he met Adam who had been the first man on earth; and next he met Noah, then Moses and Jesus, and others including Aaron the brother of Moses, and John the Baptist who was cousin to Jesus.

At last, Muhammad came to the very highest part of heaven where grows the Tree of Heaven; and it was here that he was ☛

given the laws of the Muslim religion which is called Islam – which means 'giving yourself up to do God's will'.

On his way back down to earth, Muhammad again met Moses. 'How often a day must followers of your religion say their prayers?' asked Moses.

'Fifty, I was told,' said Muhammad.

'That is too many. No one will remember to pray fifty times a day!'

So Muhammad returned to ask for a smaller number. And, again, on his way back down, he met Moses once more.

'How many prayers are now ordered?' he asked.

'Forty.'

'That is still too many!'

Muhammad went back several times until the number of prayer times was reduced to five.

'That is still too many,' said Moses.

'I would be ashamed to return again,' said Muhammad and continued his way back to earth, down the ladder. And there Gabriel and Muhammad found Burraq waiting – and, on her back, they returned to Makka, to the very house where Gabriel had found Muhammad sleeping. They arrived just at the very moment that the first rays of sunlight announced the start of a new day. The prophet Muhammad's night journey to Jerusalem and to heaven above had taken just a few short hours.

It was many years later that Muslims built a special building in Jerusalem as a reminder of that night journey. It was a holy building, a mosque called the Dome of the Rock, and it was built on the very spot where, it is said, Muhammad climbed the ladder to heaven. What is more, it is the same spot where, centuries before, King Solomon had built *his* temple ... also to the glory of God. ◆

33

Murder in the Cathedral

This story, which will probably appeal most to younger pupils, is included for the simple reason that it is a good story and part of our cultural heritage. If it has a moral, it is that it can be extremely dangerous to lose one's temper! It is also a good example of the way in which there have always been tensions between the state and the church, between political leaders and religious leaders.

This is a true story about something that happened in England over 800 years ago. It is the story of a fairly gruesome murder, which came about entirely as the result of one man losing his temper.

◆

IT ALL BEGAN with a quarrel. Several quarrels in fact – between King Henry II of England and Thomas Becket, Archbishop of Canterbury. Once they'd been friends, really good friends. That did not last.

Henry was the most powerful king in Europe. He was king not just of England, but of much of France as well. Becket was a rich merchant's son. He had done very well for himself, getting better and better jobs (both in England and in Rome) until he had the best job of all. He became Chancellor of England. That meant he was the king's secretary and assistant. He did not do just odd jobs and write letters for him, but he was responsible for seeing that everything the king ordered was carried out.

Becket was powerful. He lived in his own palace, which was as well furnished as the king's. And, as I said, they were good friends.

☛

Now Henry was having trouble getting the leaders of the Church, the bishops, to do what he wanted. But they didn't like being bossed around by the king. They felt that even he should not tell the Church what to do. This attitude did not please Henry. Until, that is, he had an idea – what he thought was a very good idea.

He made his good friend Thomas Becket Archbishop of Canterbury. That meant that Becket would be in charge of all the bishops. Now they would have to do what Becket said, thought the king. And of course, as Becket was his friend, that would mean he would get his own way.

But that's not how it turned out. Becket *was* made Archbishop. That happened all right. But he then gave up living in luxury and lived as simply as did his own priests. What's more, he took the side of the Church. Yes, he tried to be loyal to Henry as well, but Henry now felt his old friend had turned against him. And soon they quarrelled. Seriously.

Becket had to leave England for his own safety and went to Rome. That was in the year 1164.

Six years later, in 1170, when Becket and Henry were both in France, they met and made up their quarrel. Becket returned to Canterbury. He found he was a hero. The people cheered and mobbed him as he made his way into the city. Again Becket became the champion of the Church and soon the quarrel flared up again.

Henry had always been quick to lose his temper and, one December day while he was still in France, he lost it well and truly over something that Becket had said or done. He was fuming. 'Who will rid me of this turbulent priest?' he shouted.

Four knights who heard what the king said decided he could ☞

mean only one thing. He must want Becket 'out of the way'. And so those knights, Sir William de Tracy, Reginald Fitzurse, Richard le Breton and Hugh de Merville, rode north as fast as they could and took a ship across the Channel. Some people say that Henry realised what had happened and sent messengers after them to stop them. If he did, they failed to catch up with them.

On December 29 the four knights arrived in Canterbury and met Becket. An argument took place and Becket went into the cathedral, to pray at one of the altars there. The priests of the cathedral wanted to bar and lock the doors. Becket said no: the Church of God should not be locked. Just as it was getting dark, the knights made their way into the cathedral and, there, in a holy part of the building now known as the Martyrdom, with great heavy swords, they struck down Becket and killed him.

Christians all over Europe were horrified when they heard what had happened and soon people started called him *Saint* Thomas à Becket. And it wasn't long before people began making journeys of pilgrimage to Canterbury, to pray where St Thomas was buried.

In the end, King Henry realised how much he was to blame. He too visited Canterbury to show his sorrow and to pray at the grave of his friend, Thomas. ◆

34

The Three Rings

Some time ago, a scurrilous parody of a 'consumer's test of religions' received some publicity. Which religion, it asked, was the 'best buy'? Judaism allows you to drink, Islam allows you several wives, Hinduism allows you to be reincarnated ... More seriously, it is a sad fact that people do at times attempt to compare religions in order to prove which is 'best'. This passage is included as an antidote to any such discussion. It is very loosely based on a parable told in the eighteenth-century dramatic poem 'Nathan der Weise' ('Nathan the Wise') by Gotthold Lessing. This features a Muslim, a Christian and a Jew discussing the relative merits of their religions. Nathan, a tolerant Jew, makes the point that the true religion is not a product of dogma or faith but of ethical behaviour.

Sometimes people are tempted to say that one religion is better than another. Of course the followers of any one religion will wish to believe in their religion more than in all the others. But that doesn't *prove* the others are 'wrong'. What we must do is to believe in our own religion and act upon it sincerely, as this parable tell us.

◆

ONCE UPON A time there was a wise old king. He lived in a beautiful palace and he ruled his people justly and fairly. All his people loved him and respected him; almost all of them would have laid down their lives for their king.

But what was the secret that made everybody love the king? It was a magic ring – for this king had a special ring that made its owner just and fair, kind and gentle, and pleasing in the sight of God. It had been his father's before him and, when the king should die, the ring would become the property of his son, who (in turn) would be loved by the people just as much as the ☞

old king had been. And when that son died the ring would be handed down to the next king; and so it would go from generation to generation.

So, as I said, there was this wise old king who lived in a beautiful palace and ruled his people justly and fairly. All his people loved him and respected him and the country prospered, and there was only happiness and peace in the land – because he possessed the magic ring. However (unlike his fathers before him), this particular king had *three* sons. So which should have the ring when he died?

He loved them dearly and equally. And, as he was as fair in dealing with his family as he was with the affairs of state, he could not decide which son should have the ring. When he was alone with one son, he thought he loved that son best and so he promised him the ring. And so he did with each of the others, separately.

And naturally enough, even though the king possessed untold riches, it was the desire of each of the three sons to inherit the ring rather than anything else.

Now, after a year had passed by, the old king died peacefully in his sleep, and his three sons were left, none of them having the ring. The were soon arguing as to who should have it. Each one claimed that the father had promised the ring to him, and to him alone. They parted in very bad temper, each one refusing to admit that he had not got the ring. In fact, each one pretended he had been given the ring.

In a few days' time, however, they decided to submit their case to the oldest and wisest judge in the country. But, before the hearing, each son went secretly to a jeweller and arranged for an exact replica of the ring to be made. And so on the ☛

appointed day, they presented themselves at the court, each with a ring.

The judge listened patiently to each son in turn before saying anything. Then he said, 'Each one of you puts forward a very good case. You all say that your father, who is now in heaven, promised you the ring. He may well have done. But more than likely none of these three rings is the true one; they are all copies – each one a good likeness. Now, we cannot know which is the true one: we must wait until we see the father again. Only he knows which is the genuine one.

'The original ring had the power to make its owner pleasing before God, and loved by all men. You must each believe in your own ring and try to love and be loved. In that way the true ring will show itself – if, indeed, one of these rings is the original.'

And in the same way, the true faith will show itself. ◆

35

The Best Book That Ever Was

One of Charles Dickens' least known books is his The Life of Our Lord.
*Indeed, considering his frequent attacks on sham piety and religious
humbug, it comes as something of a surprise to discover that he wrote his
own version of the Gospel story. However, he did not write it for
publication but for his own children and it was not published until 1934
when the last of his sons died. This passage may serve as an example of
(or introduction to) the work of a pre-eminent novelist or as a simple
retelling of two of the parables told by Jesus and of an incident from his
life – all three being, in their different ways, controversial. Each might
initiate a short discussion. ('Is this fair?' 'Is this a fair pay policy?' 'Did
he let her off completely?' etc.) (See also Passage No. 28.)*

One of the greatest English writers was Charles Dickens. His
stories (such as *David Copperfield* and *Oliver Twist*) appeared
as serials in popular magazines over a hundred years ago.
Some people say they were the 'soaps' of the nineteenth
century.

For his own children, he wrote down the life story of Jesus.
When each of his children grew up and left home, he gave
them a copy of it and a copy of the New Testament. He also
wrote a letter to each of them. This is part of one of those
letters:

◆

I PUT A New Testament among your books, for the very same
reasons, and with the very same hopes that made me write an
easy account of it for you, when you were a little child; because
it is the best book that ever was or will be known in the world,
and because it teaches you the best lessons by which any
human creature who tries to be truthful and faithful to duty ☛

can possibly be guided. As your brothers have gone away, one by one, I have written to each such words as I am now writing to you, and have entreated them all to guide themselves by this book, putting aside the interpretations and inventions of Man.

And this is part of Dickens' story of *The Life of Our Lord.* (Peter is one of Jesus' close friends.)

◆

Peter asked him, 'Lord, how often shall I forgive any one who offends me? Seven times?' Our Saviour answered, 'Seventy times seven times, and more than that. For how can you hope that God will forgive you, when you do wrong, unless you forgive all other people!'

And he told his disciples this story. He said, there was once a servant who owed his master a great deal of money, and could not pay it, at which the master, being very angry, was going to have this servant sold for a slave. But the servant kneeling down and begging his master's pardon with great sorrow, the master forgave him. Now this same servant had a fellow-servant who owed him a hundred pence, and instead of being kind and forgiving to this poor man, as his master had been to him, he put him in prison for the debt. His master, hearing of it, went to him, and said, 'Oh wicked servant, I forgave you. Why did you not forgive your fellow-servant!' And because he had not done so, his master turned him away into great misery. 'So,' said Our Saviour, 'how can you expect God to forgive you, if you do not forgive others!' This is the meaning of that part of the Lord's Prayer, where we say 'forgive us our trespasses' – that word means faults – 'as we forgive them that trespass against us.'

And he told them another story, and said, 'There was a certain ☞

101

farmer once, who had a vineyard, and he went out early in the morning, and agreed with some labourers to work there all day, for a penny. And bye and bye, when it was later, he went out again and engaged some more labourers on the same terms; and bye and bye went out again; and so on, several times, until the afternoon. When the day was over, and they all came to be paid, those who had worked since morning complained that those who had not begun to work until late in the day had the same money as themselves, and they said it was not fair. But the master said, 'Friend, I agreed with you for a penny; and is it less money to you, because I give the same money to another man?'

Our Saviour meant to teach them by this that people who have done good all their lives long will go to Heaven after they are dead. But that people who have been wicked, because of their being miserable, or not having parents and friends to take care of them when young, and who are truly sorry for it, however late in their lives, and pray God to forgive them, will be forgiven and will go to Heaven too. He taught his disciples in these stories, because he knew the people liked to hear them, and would remember what he said better, if he said it in that way. They are called parables – the parables of Our Saviour.

The people listened to all that Our Saviour said, but were not agreed among themselves about him. The Pharisees and Jews had spoken to some of them against him, and some of them were inclined to do him harm and even to murder him. But they were afraid as yet, to do him any harm, because of his goodness, and his looking so divine and grand – although he was very simply dressed, almost like the poor people – that they could hardly bear to meet his eyes.

One morning, he was sitting in a place called the Mount of Olives, teaching the people who were all clustered round him, listening and learning attentively, when a great noise was heard, and a crowd of Pharisees, and some other great people like them, called scribes, came running in, with great cries and shouts, dragging among them a woman who had done wrong. And they all cried out together, 'Master! Look at this woman. The law says she shall be pelted with stones until she is dead. But what say you? What say you?'

Jesus looked upon the noisy crowd attentively, and knew that they had come to make him say the law was wrong and cruel; and that if he said so, they would make it a charge against him and would kill him. They were ashamed and afraid as he looked into their faces, but they still cried out, 'Come! What say you master? What say you?'

Jesus stooped down, and wrote with his finger in the sand on the ground. 'He that is without sin among you, let him throw the first stone at her.' As they read this, looking over one another's shoulders, and as he repeated the words to them, they went away, one by one, ashamed, until not a man of all the noisy crowd was left there; and Jesus Christ, and the woman, hiding her face in her hands, alone remained.

Then said Jesus Christ, 'Woman, where are thine accusers? Hath no man condemned thee?' She answered, trembling, 'No, Lord!' Then said Our Saviour, 'Neither do I condemn thee. Go! and sin no more!' ◆

CHARLES DICKENS

36

Serious Illness

This is an excerpt from a volume of autobiography called Bright Morning *by the journalist, radio dramatist and television film-maker, Don Haworth. Its subtitle is 'Images of a Lancashire Boyhood' and this particular account describes how his young brother became ill with diphtheria (a potentially fatal illness in 1935). It is a salutary reminder of how much we sometimes take for granted the improvements in health care.*

This true story tells what happened when a small boy caught diphtheria in a Lancashire town about sixty years ago. Diphtheria is a serious infectious disease of the throat which makes breathing difficult. At that time it could be very serious indeed. This passage is a reminder of how much doctors and nurses can do for us now when we are ill, and it also reminds us what it's like when you have to go into hospital. You might think about what makes a good hospital visitor . . .

◆

ONE MORNING IN the January of 1935 my brother Eric, then seven, woke with the symptoms of a cold heavy enough to keep him off school. He had his breakfast in bed, then got up and sat looking at books by the fire. In the afternoon he became more ill and was put to bed. When I got home from school towards dusk my mother and grandmother were discussing whether he was bad enough to justify disturbing the doctor. I asked what was the matter. Neither of them could bring themselves to pronounce what they suspected. They decided they ought to call the doctor, and my mother walked down to the telephone at Towneley station. Snow was falling heavily. Dr Dixon angrily asked her if she couldn't see the weather. He would come first thing in the morning.

When my grandfather arrived home it was apparent to him that the morning might not be soon enough. He tramped down to the surgery and asked the doctor to come at once. Harry Dixon, a heavy man who wheezed through Turkish cigarettes, normally had a soft spot for him and addressed him as 'grandpa', but faced with an expedition up the hill in snow, he swore. How could he get up there in his car? Why hadn't they sent for him in the morning? How could he turn out and leave the waiting-room full of patients? They argued back and forth, my grandfather, according to his own account, saying little.

'Anyway,' Harry Dixon concluded. 'I'm not turning out tonight. I'll come in the morning.'

'Very well, doctor,' my grandfather said. 'And if the boy isn't with us in the morning –'

He left the question unfinished and walked down the passage and out into the snow. Behind him the doors were yanked open. 'Grandpa,' Harry Dixon shouted, 'I'll come.'

The doctor made the last part of the journey up the steepest part of the hill on foot and arrived wheezing and angry. He clumped upstairs, shedding clots of snow. He complained of being called so late. He complained of the dismal light in the bedroom. He rammed a dessert-spoon handle into Eric's mouth and said so fiercely I could hear him downstairs, 'Come on, keep your mouth open. How do you expect me to see?'

But when he could see he calmed down. 'It's diphtheria,' he said. 'I'll send for the ambulance.'

My father came home from work. The ambulance men carried Eric out to their vehicle wrapped in a big red blanket. The last boy I had seen carried into the fever ambulance had cheerfully called to onlookers. He died within three weeks. My brother was carried out worse. His head lolled. He was incapable of saying anything.

The ambulance slid and slewed down the snowbound road. We sat late by the dying fire without speaking. My mother looked old.

Next day, a Saturday, was visiting day at the hospital. Children were not allowed to visit at all and adults were not allowed beyond the matron's office for fear of contracting the disease. A catwalk had been built round the outer walls which parents mounted to shout in through the window to the patients. It sounded like a market. But my brother was too ill to respond with more than a faint smile. When they came home I could see they thought he would die.

A bulletin from the hospital was posted each day at noon outside the bus office in Burnley town centre, and we got the same information earlier by telephoning the hospital from Towneley station. It amounted to little. The patients were placed in three categories: seriously ill, ill, and making satisfactory progress. Nobody would divulge any more than that.

My brother remained on the 'seriously ill' list. We followed the bulletin each day, dreading the disappearance of his number.

Then one day in February he was out of the top category and listed among the 'ill'. It was as though the spring had arrived. But it was a false blossoming and soon he was back among the 'seriously ill'. It was not a relapse so much as the onset of a secondary malady. The serum had attacked his heart, and now he had to lie for weeks with the foot of his bed raised on blocks. Death claimed many at this stage. He made progress, then relapsed. He was four months in hospital before the battle was won. ◆

DON HAWORTH

37

Priscilla and the Wimps

This is an escapist, but at the same time very satisfying, American story about one way of dealing with a school bully.

You probably know what it's like when you come up against a bully – against someone whom you seem to have no way of fighting, the sort of bully that *no one* seems able to tackle. This is a story from America about how one such bully was finally dealt with.

◆

LISTEN, THERE WAS a time when you couldn't even go the *rest room* around this school without a pass. And I'm not talking about those little pink tickets made out by some teacher. I'm talking about a pass that could cost anywhere up to a buck, sold by Monk Klutter.

Not that Mighty Monk ever touched money, not in public. The gang he ran, which ran the school for him, was his collection agency. They were Klutter's Kobras, a name spelled out in nailheads on six well-known black plastic windbreakers.

Monk's threads were more . . . subtle. A pile-lined suede battle jacket with lizard-skin flaps over tailored Levis and a pair of ostrich-skin boots, brass-toed and suitable for kicking people around. One of his Kobras did nothing all day but walk a half-step behind Monk, carrying a fitted bag with Monk's gym shoes, a roll of rest-room passes, a cashbox and a switchblade that Monk gave himself manicures with at lunch over the Kobras' table. ☞

Speaking of lunch, there were a few cases of advanced malnutrition among the newer kids. The ones who were a little slow in handing over a cut of their lunch money and were therefore barred from the cafeteria. Monk ran a tight ship.

I admit it. I'm five foot five, and when the Kobras slithered by, with or without Monk, I shrank. And I admit this, too: I paid up on a regular basis. And I might add: so would you.

This school was old Monk's Garden of Eden. Unfortunately for him, there was a serpent in it. The reason Monk didn't recognise trouble when it was staring him in the face is that the serpent in the Kobras' Eden was a girl.

Practically every guy in school could show you his scars. Fang marks from Kobras, you might say. And they were all highly visible in the shower room: lumps, lacerations, blue bruises, you name it. But girls usually got off with a warning.

Except there was this one girl named Priscilla Roseberry. Picture a girl named Priscilla Roseberry, and you'll be light years off. Priscilla was, hands down, the largest student in our particular institution of learning. I'm not talking fat. I'm talking big. Even beautiful, in a bionic way. Priscilla wasn't inclined towards organised crime. Otherwise, she could have put together a gang that would turn Klutter's Kobras into garter snakes.

Priscilla was basically a loner except she had one friend. A little guy named Melvin Detweiler. You talk about The Odd Couple. Melvin's one of the smallest guys above midget status ever seen. A really nice guy, but, you know – little. They even had lockers next to each other, in the same bank as mine. I don't know what they had going. I'm not saying this was a romance. After all, people deserve their privacy.

Priscilla was sort of above everything, if you'll pardon a pun. ☞

And very calm, as only the very big can be. If there was anybody who didn't notice Klutter's Kobras, it was Priscilla.

Until one winter day after school when we were all grabbing our coats out of our lockers. And hurrying, since Klutter's Kobras made sweeps of the corridors for after-school shakedowns.

Anyway, up to Melvin's locker swaggers one of the Kobras. Never mind his name. Gang members don't need names. They've got group identity. He reaches down and grabs little Melvin by the neck and slams his head against his locker door. The sound of skull against steel rippled all the way down the locker row, speeding the crowds on their way.

'OK, let's see your pass,' snarls the Kobra.

'A pass for what this time?' Melvin asks, probably still dazed.

'Let's call it a pass for very short people,' says the Kobra, 'a dwarf tax.' He wheezes a little Kobra chuckle at his own wittiness. And already he's reaching for Melvin's wallet with the hand that isn't circling Melvin's windpipe. All this time, of course, Melvin and the Kobra are standing in Priscilla's big shadow.

She's taking her time shoving her books into her locker and pulling on a very large-size coat. Then, quicker than the eye, she brings the side of her enormous hand down in a chop that breaks the Kobra's hold on Melvin's throat. You could hear a pin drop in that hallway. Nobody'd ever laid a finger on a Kobra, let alone a hand the size of Priscilla's.

Then Priscilla, who hardly ever says anything to anybody except to Melvin, says to the Kobra, 'Who's your leader, wimp?'

This practically blows the Kobra away. First he's chopped by a girl, and now she's acting like she doesn't know Monk Klutter, ☛

the Head Honcho of the World. He's so amazed, he tells her. 'Monk Klutter.'

'Never heard of him,' Priscilla mentions. 'Send him to see me.' The Kobra just backs away from her like the whole situation is too big for him, which it is.

Pretty soon Monk himself slides up. He jerks his head once, and his Kobras slither off down the corridor. He's going to handle this interesting case personally. 'Who is it around here doesn't know Monk Klutter?'

He's standing inches from Priscilla, but since he'd have to look up at her, he doesn't. 'Never heard of him,' says Priscilla.

Monk's not happy with this answer, but by now he's spotted Melvin, who's grown smaller in spite of himself. Monk breaks his own rule by reaching for Melvin with his own hands. 'Kid,' he says, 'you're going to have to educate your girl friend.'

His hands never quite make it to Melvin. In a move of pure poetry Priscilla has Monk in a hammerlock. His neck's popping like gunfire, and his head's bowed under the immense weight of her forearm. His suede jacket's peeling back, showing pile.

Priscilla's behind him in another easy motion. And with a single mighty thrust forward, frog-marches Monk into her own locker. It's incredible. His ostrich-skin boots click once in the air. And suddenly he's gone, neatly wedged into the locker, a perfect fit. Priscilla bangs the door shut, twirls the lock, and strolls out of school. Melvin goes with her, of course, trotting along below her shoulder. The last stragglers leave quietly.

Well, this is where fate, an even bigger force than Priscilla, steps in. It snows all that night, a blizzard. The whole town ices up. And school closes for a week. ◆

RICHARD PECK

38

A *Change of* Heart

This is an account of a girl's experiences at work. Her job is to sell space to potential advertisers in the classified columns of an evening newspaper. It is a passage that may be used in conjunction with discussion of work experience or in a careers session. It could be a useful reminder about what makes a satisfying job and what kinds of job are ultimately unacceptable.

(Note: It may be helpful to bring in a copy of an evening newspaper to show the group just what the small ads section of a newspaper looks like.)

This is a story about a young girl who starts work on an evening newspaper. Her job is to sell advertising space in the classified columns to would-be advertisers – and to persuade them to spend more than they intended by encouraging them to place longer adverts. At first she thinks it's quite a good job . . .

But do you think that this is the sort of job that you would like or that you would think was worth doing? What sorts of jobs would you refuse to do on similar grounds?

◆

'EVENING STAR CLASSIFIED, can I help you?' said a bright cheerful voice. Anne put her hand up to move her headphones, straightening the mouthpiece which by this time had drooped a little.

'We sell cars, houses and jobs. Anything that desires a market, we provide it,' said Liz Hooke, Executive Advertising Supervisor, as she stood behind a wooden stand which housed her notes. She spoke to the trainees like a priest from a pulpit. The logic was simple. ☞

'The more space they purchase, the more likely it is that their advert will be seen by the potential buyers, so the more likely that they'll sell their houses or cars or whatever.' She smiled a glowing smile and Anne wondered whether she was going to say, 'Amen'.

Anne had found this advertising business quite exciting after three years of working in the securities department of an established merchant bank. Well, that had been at first. Everybody was so nice. She had been really taken aback by the way that they were all on first-name terms with each other. This had seemed progressive. She had managed to call Liz Hooke 'Liz' after only one morning. That was unusual for Anne because normally it took her much longer than that to get to know people. There seemed to be none of those divisions between men and women that she had experienced in the bank. Liz had stated quite clearly that, 'In advertising, sex is not important.'

The trainees had tittered at this, but then Liz always was a bit of a joker. After they had stopped, she had donated a wide toothy smile to proceedings and went on, 'Success in this job depends on how well or badly we serve the customer. We are only here to help them. Advertising provides a vital service which could not be found anywhere else.' This had been Liz's finishing statement and it concluded a week of theorising on the art of advertising. Anne went home to her husband and said, 'At last, I've found a worthwhile job.'

The following Monday Anne was put into a pool where she was to begin her job. It took her until break on Wednesday afternoon to realise that all was not as it seemed.

The 'pool' was a large office not particularly noted for its interior design. It housed numerous rows of desks and at the ☞

top end of the room on a platform sat Liz. The place had the air of a Victorian schoolroom.

The 'boys and girls', as they were called, sat in these rows, attached to their desks by the wires of their headphones and waited for incoming phone calls.

Anne was sitting in the third row and spent her day facing the back of the person in front. The only person whose eyes she ever met was Liz who every now and then turned on an encouraging smile and then went immediately back to studying her nails.

The calls came thick and fast and Anne was tutored by a superior into expanding the desires of the client from two-line adverts into inch or half inch boxes with a heading in heavy, black type.

'Who'll notice two-line ads?' Liz would often ask. Another trainee, George, who remarked that his uncle often scoured the small ads for bargains, was immediately frozen by a look from Liz. She smiled before she delivered her argument, 'Yes, but there aren't many like him, are there George?' George only lasted a few weeks. 'He couldn't cope,' Liz said at the weekly pep talk.

Business was good, and commission was a topic which was discussed in every spare moment. There were those who always did well and so treated the subject as an irrelevancy. Those who did badly also viewed the subject from this angle, although from different motives. The main bulk of the operators were those who bordered from average to good. It was these people who jealously counted up each line gained and translated it into pennies and pounds. Anne had fitted somewhere within this group.

When she had first realised that her job did not involve her being a kind of consumer welfare worker, she had made excuses, 'Well, people have to have somewhere to advertise, don't they? And they need professional people to help advise them.' A few weeks later she was heard to say, 'They make money selling their cars and houses, don't they? Why shouldn't we make some too?' And a month or so later: 'It's just a job. I might as well make as much as I can while I'm here'.

It was about a week after that Anne had decided to try and break her record commission level. It was Thursday afternoon and she was slightly ahead of her target for the day. It was five twenty-five and she decided to make the next call her last before going home. 'Make it a detached house in Barnet,' she thought. That was an inch and half block or maybe even a mini display. In fact the voice of an old woman came over her earphones. She sounded a little distant and Anne said in her nicest voice, 'Could you speak up a little, dear?' The old woman was mumbling something about a lost pet and Anne felt a sense of impatience. It was five thirty and she wanted to get home. A lost pet ad wasn't worth a light.

'Look dear, can you speak a little more slowly,' she said in a harsher voice. No point in putting on the niceties, Anne thought, this is definitely a two-liner. The old woman began again, and Anne began to copy down the details. She contemplated cutting her off. Then she could go home. The two-line advert would only cut down her overall average. She looked up at Liz who was sitting in her usual position and who, it had been rumoured, had a tiny earphone which meant that she could cut into any call at any time. She couldn't risk cutting the old dear off. Her mind went back to the call and she instantly realised that the old woman was crying. Her cat had ☛

disappeared the day before yesterday. Did she think it could have got run over, or taken away? What did she think? Anne was stumped by this. This wasn't in the script. How the hell should she know whether it had got run over or not? Her anger turned to pity and she tried to draw the old woman around. She stopped crying, and Anne began to word the advert. She felt touchy and the back of her throat felt tight and sore. She read the price of the advert over to the woman.

'Oh, I couldn't afford that, dear,' said the old woman in a crackly voice. After a moment or two's hesitation she rang off. 'What a waste of time,' Anne thought. Surely the old girl knew the price of adverts? She totalled up her lines for the day and went off home. She felt annoyed. Her depression increased on the train and she spent the evening in a bad mood.

The next day was slow, and it was obvious to Anne that she would not break her commission level. She thought about the cat. And the old lady. She was hot and tired and went to the ladies room. She found herself crying. 'She would have been better ringing the local paper anyway,' Anne thought. 'It's not my problem. It's not my job to find her cat.'

Liz was horrified to find one of her very favourite op's in this emotional state and immediately sent her home with a packet of Panadol and a sympathetic expression.

Anne stayed for another few weeks and then handed in her notice. When Liz asked her why, she said, 'I just don't know. I can't put my finger on it.' ◆

ANNE GEBBETT

39

Mini-sagas

In 1988 the Sunday Telegraph *magazine, in conjunction with the BBC Radio 4* Today *programme, ran a 'mini-saga' competition. The rules were simple: to write a mini-saga – that is, a complete story of exactly fifty words. It must have a beginning, a middle and an end. These are some of the winning entries.*

Each one may be used on its own as a separate reading, for each has its own provocative discussion point or moral. Alternatively, they may be used as examples to inspire a group to compile their own 'anthology for assembly' of mini-sagas.

The story I'm going to read you now is a very short one – it has just fifty words. You will have to listen very carefully to get its point . . .

◆

We've Always Been a Close-knit Family

'There's only
the two of us left now.
You've got to be grateful
to those transplant pioneers,
back in the 80s. I'd have been
dead ten years but for Ron's
lungs and Auntie Kitty's liver
and kidneys. I'll be needing
a change of heart soon.
How are you feeling,
George?'

GERALDINE COX ☞

Invincible

He will not live, they said.
He is now thirty-one.
He will not walk, they said.
He ran the London Marathon.
He will not be independent,
they said.
He owns a flat in town.
He'll be a loser all his life,
they said.
He beat them all,
hands down.

JANE GRINAWAY (AGED 14)

Out of the Mouths of Babes?

'Come and meet my friend on
Sports Day, Mummy.'
Sports Day came.
'Where's your new friend, Paul?'
'He's sitting on the front
bench.'
There were ten on the front
bench.
'He's wearing red shorts.'
There were three boys with
red shorts.
'His hair's curly.'
'Oh, the black one,'
said Mummy.

KATHRYN CLARKE (AGED 15)

40

The Last Flower

This passage is a fable by the American humourist James Thurber. It was originally a series of cartoon drawings and each of the following lines was the caption to a separate cartoon. It may be used as a simple reading with its own clear message. Alternatively (and very much more ambitiously), it may become the narrative for a mime presentation or it could be fully dramatised or illustrated by students.

This story is called 'The Last Flower'. It tells what happens at some point in the future – to be precise, after World War XII. It is up to you to decide whether it has a happy ending.

◆

WORLD WAR XII, as everybody knows, brought about the collapse of civilisation.

Towns, cities, and villages disappeared from the earth.

All the groves and forests were destroyed, and all the gardens, and all the works of art.

Men, women, and children became lower than the lower animals.

Discouraged and disillusioned, dogs deserted their fallen masters.

Emboldened by the pitiful condition of the former lords of the earth, rabbits descended upon them.

Books, paintings, and music disappeared from the earth, and human beings just sat around doing nothing.

Years and years went by.

Even the few Generals who were left forgot what the last war had decided.

Boys and girls grew up to stare at each other blankly, for love had passed from the earth.

☞

One day a young girl who had never seen a flower chanced to
    come upon the last one in the world.
She told the other human beings that the last flower was
    dying.
The only one who paid any attention to her was a young man
    she found wandering about.
Together the young man and the girl nurtured the flower and
    it began to live again.
One day a bee visited the flower, and a hummingbird.
Before long there were two flowers, and then four, and then a
    great many.
Groves and forests flourished again.
The young girl began to take an interest in how she looked.
The young man discovered that touching the girl was
    pleasurable.
Love was reborn into the world.
Their children grew up strong and healthy and learned to run
    and laugh.
Dogs came out of their exile.
The young man discovered, by putting one stone upon
    another, how to build a shelter.
Pretty soon everybody was building shelters.
Towns, cities, and villages sprang up.

Song came back into the world,
And troubadours and jugglers
And tailors and cobblers
And painters and poets
And sculptors and wheelwrights
And soldiers
And Lieutenants and Captains
And Generals and Major-Generals
And liberators.

Some people went one place to live, and some another.

Before long, those who went to live in the valleys wished they
 had gone to live in the hills,

And those who had gone to live in the hills wished they had
 gone to live in the valleys.

The liberators, under the guidance of God, set fire to the
 discontent,

So presently the World was at war again.

This time the destruction was so complete . . .

That nothing at all was left in the World –

Except one man

And one woman

And one flower. ◆

JAMES THURBER

THE GREAT, THE GOOD AND THE HOLY

The seeds of godlike power are in us still:
Gods are we, bards, saints, heroes, if we will.

MATTHEW ARNOLD

41

Ibrahim

For Jews, Abraham is one of the founding fathers of their religion. For the followers of Islam, he is the 'first Muslim'. Ibrahim is the Arabic version of the name 'Abraham'.

Ibrahim, along with Moses, is the most frequently mentioned prophet in the Qur'an. The Qur'an tells Muslims that Ibrahim rejected the worship of the sun, moon and stars and turned to the one creator God. Ibrahim is also said to have rebuilt the Ka'ba – the story of which is the subject of this reading.

For Muslims, the most important building in the whole world is the Ka'ba. The word means 'cube' – and that is what it is. A granite building in the shape of a cube: 12 metres long, 10 metres wide and 15 metres high.

Muslims believe it was built by Adam. After he had been sent away from the Garden of Eden where he first lived, Adam travelled for a long time. Eventually he came to a place he believed was the centre point of all the land, and there (as God had told him to do) he built the Ka'ba as a house of praise to God.

But the years went by and men forgot what the building was for. It was covered by sand, and then destroyed by the Great Flood in the time of Noah.

And so we come to the time of the man whom some call Abraham and whom Muslims call Ibrahim – and that's who this reading is about.

◆

ONE DAY, IBRAHIM had a dream in which God commanded him to sacrifice his son Ismail. Ibrahim was so obedient to God's will he was prepared to do this, but as soon as Ibrahim started to carry out the deed he heard a voice. He turned round and saw a sheep caught in a bush. 'Ibrahim,' said the voice, 'kill this sheep in the place of Ismail, for you are a loyal servant.'

And that is what Ibrahim did. But after that, God sent Ismail to live in a place far away from there. And that place was Makka.

Ibrahim prayed to God that he might be able to see Ismail again. At last, God told him to set off on the long and difficult journey to Makka, and to build the House of God in that place.

As soon as Ibrahim arrived in Makka, he got off his camel and went to a well called Zam-zam. There was Ismail. Ibrahim told his son what God had commanded him, and so they began work. Ismail fetched stones from the nearby hills and Ibrahim laid them, to form a new Ka'ba. They worked each day from sunrise to sunset and, as they worked, Ibrahim prayed: 'O God, accept our offering. You, the All-hearing; you, the All-knowing. O God, let us remain your followers so that we may become the family of Islam. Show us the way to worship and have mercy on us – for you are the All-forgiving and the All-loving.'

The last stone that Ibrahim set in place was a special stone (said to have been brought from Heaven by the Angel Gabriel). It's still there, in the south-east corner of the Ka'ba.

When the work was finished, Ibrahim and Ismail kissed that stone in praise of God – and were astonished to see that, when they kissed it, the stone shone with the love of God, for this was the very place where Adam had built the first Ka'ba. The ☛

new Ka'ba was kept holy for many years, but later the purpose of the building was forgotten.

Until, that is, many hundreds of years later, the prophet Muhammad cleansed and re-dedicated this cube-shaped building as a place of worship to the one God.

And today, when Muslims make a holy journey or pilgrimage to the Ka'ba in Makka, they know they are following not only in the footsteps of the prophet Muhammad but also in those of Adam – and of Ibrahim and his son Ismail. ◆

42

The Reluctant Leader

*Although Jews claim descent from Abraham, it was Moses who gave
them the concept that they were the chosen people; Moses who led them
out of Egypt, received the Law on Mount Sinai, and shaped their nation.
Yet Moses, the greatest of Jewish leaders, was reluctant to take up the
role, as is recorded in the third chapter of the book of Exodus. Besides
teaching something of the life of Moses, this reading is on the subject of
leadership – its responsibilities and requirements. Who makes a good
leader?*

Some people want to boss everything – whether it's a soccer
team or just a group of friends forming a new club or gang. Up
goes their hand. 'Me! Me! I'll do it. I'll be captain. I'll be the
leader. Go on, let me . . .'

Doesn't mean they'll make the best leader – but that doesn't
stop them wanting the job.

But not everyone wants to be a leader. Some people really
dread the idea – hate the thought of having to be 'in charge'.
'Oh no,' they say. 'Not me. Someone else. So-and-so's good at
organising people. Let them do it.'

But what's it like if you don't want to be a leader, but you're
forced into it? Like when a teacher's going to be out of the
classroom for a while. 'Right, now while I'm out, I'm leaving
Verity in charge. She's sensible – so you must all do what she
says.' And that's the last thing Verity wants. She hates
speaking up, hates having to be the boss . . .

YEARS AND YEARS ago – well, centuries and centuries ago to be accurate (in the time of the Old Testament) – it was just the same for Moses. Except in his case, it was God who was insisting he be leader – leader of all the Jewish people. And what's more, God told Moses he'd got to arrange their escape from Egypt, the country where they were being kept as slaves.

It all began out on the hills. Moses was working as a shepherd, looking after some sheep that belonged to his father-in-law. Suddenly he noticed an amazing sight. A bush. On fire. Nothing especially amazing about that, except that the flames weren't destroying the bush. It was burning without being eaten up by the fire. Moses went closer to see what it was. And as he did, he heard a voice – coming from the burning bush. And Moses knew that it was God speaking to him.

God told Moses how he wanted him to be the leader of the Jewish people. He was to speak to the ruler of Egypt (who was called the Pharaoh) and to say that he, the Pharaoh, was to let the Jews leave Egypt. The thought of it terrified Moses.

'Why me?' he said. 'I'll be a useless leader.'

'Don't worry,' said the voice of God. 'I'll be with you. I'll give you strength.'

'But the Jewish people won't believe me. They won't accept me as their leader.'

'You must tell them that I, the Lord God, have given you authority to be their leader.'

'But,' said Moses, still worked up at the thought of having to do all this, 'even if the Jewish people accept me, the Egyptians won't do what I say.'

'I shall give you power,' said the Lord God, 'power to perform signs that will convince the Pharaoh and all the Egyptians.'

'I'm still useless as a leader,' replied Moses. 'I'm no good at persuading people, getting them to do what I say. I'm hopeless at speaking in public –'

'Don't worry. I'll be with you. And your brother Aaron will help. You'll tell him what to say and he'll speak out all right . . .'

And that's what happened. Moses, who felt he was the last person on this earth suited to be a leader, became one of the most famous leaders in all history. The Jewish people did what he said; he persuaded the Pharaoh (in the end) to let them all leave Egypt – *and* Moses was able to lead them to freedom in their own country. God had not, after all, asked him to do something impossible. ◆

43

Alien Corn

This passage is a retelling of the story of Ruth, who is the subject of the eighth book of the Old Testament (and great-grandmother of King David). This short romantic tale tells how Ruth leaves her own land to go with her widowed mother-in-law, Naomi, to Bethlehem. The moral of the story as it is told in the Bible is one of religious tolerance: Ruth may be a foreigner, but she fulfils the Jewish law. As the story is retold here, it emphasises the quality of being prepared to put the needs of others before one's immediate desires.

This reading is a romance: it ends happily ever after, with the central character, Ruth, marrying a wealthy farmer. It is also a reminder that one day we shall need to care for our parents, just as they have cared for us when we were young.

◆

FIRST CAME THE bad news; then the good news. Then more bad news – followed by more . . . bad news. One thing after another, that's what it seemed like.

It all began with the famine, and a really serious lack of food in the land then called Palestine. It was especially around the little town called Bethlehem. And that's where the family lived: Elimelech and his wife Naomi, and their two growing sons. Eventually, they decided there was nothing for it. They would have to leave their home and go in search of food. They travelled eastwards, across the River Jordan to a foreign country known as the Land of Moab.

They may have been strangers there, but they found food and somewhere to live – so that was good news. And the two boys grew up and married local Moabite girls called Orpah and Ruth. ☛

It was then that things went wrong again.

Elimelech died, and then (to make it much worse) so did his two sons. That left Naomi, Orpah and Ruth – all without husbands, and in those days it was almost impossible for a family to survive without a husband or father.

Naomi, who was getting old now, decided she would rather go back to her own country where she had friends, especially as she had heard the famine was now over.

So the three of them started out together. They hadn't gone far when Naomi stopped. 'Listen,' she said to Orpah and Ruth. 'You must stay in your own country. That's where you belong and that's where you'll find new husbands.' Neither of them wanted to leave Naomi but, in the end, Orpah decided she'd stay. Ruth thought otherwise. 'Don't ask me to leave you. Wherever you go, I'll go. Wherever you want to live, I'll live.'

Naomi knew she wasn't going to change Ruth's mind, so they travelled on together. Ruth was determined to help Naomi, but unsure what it would be like to live in a strange country.

They arrived back in Bethlehem in April, at the time of the barley harvest. Even though Naomi was glad to be back and to see old friends again, she had her worries – for she did not know how two widows could earn a living.

But there was a law in those days which, at harvest time, allowed poor people to pick up all the waste ears of corn and barley that were dropped on the ground.

So Ruth spent her time walking behind the people who were gathering in the harvest, feeling very lonely, very much a foreigner in an alien land, but picking up anything they dropped – ready to take it back to Naomi to use to make bread.

One day, the rich man who owned all the fields round there ☞

noticed Ruth. Boaz, as he was called, spoke to his foreman. 'Who's that young woman over there?'

The man answered, 'She's that foreign girl, the one who came back from the Land of Moab to help look after Naomi.' Now Boaz was a distant relative of Naomi, so he went over to Ruth and told her that, when she was hungry or thirsty, she could eat and drink with his workers.

Ruth was surprised. 'Why should you be so kind to a stranger?'

Boaz told her how he knew about the death of her husband and her father, and how she had come to a foreign country to look after Naomi. 'For what you've done, you deserve a reward.'

And later that afternoon, he secretly told his workers to drop some barley or corn on purpose – so Ruth would have more to take home.

Well, that night Ruth went home and told Naomi all that had happened. That gave Naomi an idea. In those days, there was another law that said that if a woman's husband died, her close relatives should look after her. But was Ruth a really *close* relative of Boaz? Did the law apply to her?

Naomi decided to send Ruth to Boaz and ask him if he would indeed look after her. When Boaz heard what Ruth was asking, he thought for a moment and then said he would have to make certain arrangements.

And what were they? Well, Boaz in fact arranged a wedding – between himself and Ruth. So, after all the bad news came more good news – and Ruth knew that, although things had seemed to have gone wrong, God had not forgotten her. She'd been lonely, but she'd not been alone. And because she'd known what it was like to be lonely, she now knew how good it was to have kind friends and a kind husband once again. ◆

44

Mephibosheth

Mephibosheth must be one of the least-known characters in the Old Testament. There are four references to him in the second book of Samuel. He was the son of Jonathan and grandson of King Saul. When the throne passed to David, Mephibosheth (along with other members of Saul's family) were 'marginalised'. This story is developed in particular from references to Mephibosheth in 2 Samuel. 4.4 and 2 Samuel. 9.1. Besides describing an interesting biblical character, it teaches us something about what it is like to cope with a handicap.

Almost all of us have, at some time or other, been alarmed when we have been told 'to go and see' someone in authority. This is a story of a teenager in the Bible who was summoned to the royal palace to see the king. He had good reason to be afraid, and he also had the problem of coping with the handicap of lameness.

———————————————— ◆ ————————————————

MEPHIBOSHETH WAS SCARED. Not that excited, giggly feeling you get when you're not sure what's going to happen next but you hope it might be something quite nice after all . . .

No, really scared. All sort of empty in his stomach and numb. And feeling that real trouble must be about to happen, trouble he wouldn't be able to cope with.

You see, he'd been sent a message that he was to go to see the king. King David himself, in his palace! In Jerusalem! All right, so having to go to see someone important can make you *nervous,* but what was making him *scared* was that the last time any of his family were sent for like this, they didn't come back. ☞

He was only young when that happened and he hadn't understood what it was all about. The grown-ups wouldn't explain, but it was something to do with things that had happened in the war. Two of his uncles and five cousins had been sent for, they went to the palace . . . and were never seen or heard of again.

Mephibosheth had almost no relatives. His father was killed in that same war when he was five. And the war was why Mephibosheth had two legs that just wouldn't support his weight. A cripple, some people called him. During the war, news had come that his father and grandfather had been killed and the fighting was getting closer. Everyone said the family should try to escape. As I said, Mephibosheth was only five at the time, and (because they were then a rich family) he was being looked after by a nurse. Well, she picked him up and started to run, but managed to drop him. It wasn't funny. Somehow, both his ankles broke and there wasn't time to set the bones properly. They healed all wrong and ever since he had had to use crutches. He couldn't join in games with other boys and became the one who was always left out: 'The boy who was different.'

He was looked after by people who'd known his father. They felt sorry for him but they also thought he was a nuisance, something they wished they'd never taken on. He'd never be able to join the army and he wouldn't be able to farm the land, not properly – but then, out of the blue, came this message.

What I haven't told you yet is that his grandfather, Saul, was the king before King David. But as I said, his grandad and father were killed in the war. And Mephibosheth's father, whose name was Jonathan, had been a great friend of David. Then David became king and after the war there was that business about his uncles and cousins . . . So, one way and another, ☛

Mephibosheth had grown up having nothing to do with palace life and court officials. He was no longer King Saul's grandson, he was just 'the cripple lad who can't do a proper day's work'. Until he got that message, that is.

So he went to Jerusalem to see the king. If you say it like that, it sounds easy. What really happened was, he spent three days talking to different people in the village, trying to persuade one of the farmers to lend him a donkey on which to ride there. You can't blame them for not wanting to lend him one. I don't think anyone expected ever to see him again. But in the end, yes, one old man did lend him his donkey. Poor creature, it was hardly up to the journey any more than he was, but off they went.

Mephibosheth didn't have *all* that much trouble finding people who'd help him get on and off the donkey, but it's amazing how many people are nervous of touching someone who's got a handicap. Yet somehow they eventually arrived in Jerusalem and it all seemed suddenly much more frightening.

Then, as now, it was a very busy place and everyone seemed to know where they were going. Except Mephibosheth. He had to ask the way, and it sounded daft, when he was heaving himself along on crutches, with an ancient donkey limping along behind him and saying, 'Excuse me, could you tell me the way to the king's palace?' Eventually he found his way there. The palace guards, huge men in armour, seemed to be expecting him, which made it worse.

Someone led the donkey away to give it water and he was left to wait for what seemed like three days. He kept thinking what they could do to him. Beat him. Prison. Worse! He tried to practise things to say, like 'Thank you for asking me.' 'Please have mercy on me, I haven't done anything wrong and I was only a young boy when all that other business happened . . . ' ☞

Then he was sent for. That walk! That *hobble!* Along a huge corridor, then he found himself in a big room. The king was there. Mephibosheth felt as if he was swaying. He tried to bow, but the shiny, polished floor caused him to drop one of his crutches. It clattered to the ground. He bent down, trying to pick it up . . . and then the king came towards him. King David. And he bent down and picked it up and gave it to Mephibosheth. And he smiled. 'Mephibosheth,' he said, and Mephibosheth couldn't say anything. But the king must have known how his visitor felt because he said, 'Don't be afraid.' And then he started talking about all sorts of things: about Jonathan and about how he, David, and Jonathan had been the best of friends and how he'd wept when Jonathan was killed and how he hadn't known any of the family was still alive, but now he saw Mephibosheth it was like seeing Jonathan again and he wanted to do something for him.

And David went on about a promise he'd made and how he was giving Mephibosheth all the land that had belonged to his grandfather. And there was an old servant called Ziba. And King David was arranging that not only Ziba was to be Mephibosheth's servant, but that all Ziba's family were to work for him – looking after the land he'd been given. And the king also said that he could stay in the royal palace and eat with him at his table. And so it was lucky Mephibosheth had the land to bring in some money, because if you're going to live in a royal palace, you need money. Even if the food comes free, you've still got to buy clothes and things. And pay servants . . .

But it was all . . . confusing. It wasn't living in a palace that was strange. It wasn't having meals with the king. And it wasn't being rich and having servants that was special. It was the thought that he *mattered.* That someone not only cared about him, but took the trouble to show it. ☞

Much later, Mephibosheth heard from old Ziba how it had all come about . King David had sent for *him* one day, knowing that he'd been one of his grandfather's servants. And the king had asked him if there were any of King Saul's family still alive because he'd made a promise to help them if he could, out of his friendship for Jonathan. And even when Ziba told him Mephibosheth had a handicap, King David didn't back off or anything. Because some people did in those days – as they still do. They don't want to have anything to do with someone who's different in some way. No, King David sent for him and so here he was – and that was what was important to Mephibosheth: not the money, not living in a palace, but knowing that someone thought he mattered. ◆

45

Esther the Good and Haman the Wicked

Esther was a Jewish heroine who became queen to Xerxes, King of Persia. Because the king favoured her, she was able to save her people from destruction planned by the wicked Haman. The Jewish festival of Purim, which occurs one month before Passover and therefore falls in either February or March, commemorates her story. When the book of Esther is read in the synagogue on this festival, children make as much noise as they can every time the villain Haman is mentioned. Besides hissing and stamping their feet, they use football rattles, whistles and even dustbin lids. The aim is to drown Haman's name with noise. Although too much noise may not be desirable in every assembly situation, suitable moments for 'audience reaction' are indicated in this passage.

This is a story from the Bible about a woman called Esther. It is also a story about good guys and bad guys: guys who get to be important and powerful – and then become cruel. It's the story of a beautiful girl called Esther and of a wicked man called . . . Haman! ! ! [*storyteller may encourage a low hiss.*]

◆

IT ALL TOOK place long ago in a country called Persia. Its king was a man some called Xerxes, but others called Ahasuerus. We'll call him Xerxes. And in those days there lived in Persia many Jewish people, including Esther. Her parents had both died and she'd been brought up by a cousin, Mordecai, who was much older than she was.

So this is a story about four people. ☛

King Xerxes.
Beautiful Esther.
Her cousin Mordecai.
And wicked Haman. [*Another hiss or boo*]

It all began when King Xerxes quarrelled with his wife and started looking for a new queen. As soon as he saw Esther, he knew that she was the one. And that's what happened: Esther became Queen Esther. But on Mordecai's advice, she didn't tell him she was a Jew and not a Persian. Just in case, he said, it made him quarrel again.

Now not long after all this, Mordecai heard of a plot to kill King Xerxes. Mordecai told Esther. She told Xerxes. He checked it all out. It was true. And he was so pleased with Mordecai that he had his name noted down in all the state papers as 'Official Hero'. Well, time went by until a man we've heard of, a man called . . . Haman [*another hiss or boo*] became chief minister. Xerxes told everyone they must bow down in respect of him.

Mordecai (who didn't think much of this new chief minister) refused to bow down low to him, as if he was worshipping him. This made the new minister hate Mordecai and wonder how he might get his own back on him.

In the end, wicked Haman [*hisses and boos*] decided to get his revenge not just on Mordecai, but on every Jew in Persia. He persuaded King Xerxes that all the Jews in the country should be put to death on a certain day. Mordecai went straight to Esther: 'You must go to the king and beg him not to let this happen. You can't let this happen to your people.'

So Esther went to the king.

'Please, your majesty, my husband, I should like you and . . . ☞

(she avoided using the name) your chief minister to come to a banquet I am preparing for you tonight.'

And that's what happened.

It was a splendid banquet and the king and the minister were thoroughly enjoying it; they were both in a splendid mood. Esther decided to be patient. She asked them to come to another, even better, banquet the next night.

'Delighted,' they both said and each set off for home.

On his way, wicked Haman [*the boos might be increasingly angry from now on*] met Mordecai. Once again, Mordecai refused to bow down to evil Haman [*boos and hisses*]. This made the chief minister furious. He arranged to have a tall gallows built on which he could have Mordecai hanged by the neck.

Meanwhile, that same night, the king was unable to get to sleep. He wanted someone to read him a story. And the story he was read was one from the state papers. It told how, some time back, a man called Mordecai had saved him from a murderous plot. Xerxes had forgotten all about Mordecai, but decided, next morning, to reward him.

Meanwhile, Haman [*boos*] was just arriving at the palace, ready to ask permission to have Mordecai put to death. 'Your majesty,' he said.

'Ah yes,' said the king. 'I've decided to honour a certain man.'

'Would it be me?' smirked the minister.

'No,' said the king.

'Oh.' The minister was crest-fallen.

'No,' said the king. 'It's a man called Mordecai.'

'That's all ri – What? You said Mordecai!'

'Yes. Send him my second-best royal robes and arrange for him to ride through the city on a royal horse. See it all goes right, won't you?'

The wicked minister was *livid*. There was nothing he could do about it, though. He had to carry out the king's orders.

Well, the time soon came for the second banquet. The king was in a splendid mood and asked Esther if he could grant her a wish in return for the splendid banquets. Her patience had been rewarded.

'Yes,' she said. 'Spare my people, the *Jewish* people, the people who are to be put to death by Haman!' [*noise*]

The king stormed out of the room. He needed time to think. His wife was Jewish, not Persian. His chief minister, whom he'd trusted and relied on, was plotting to kill Mordecai who'd saved his life . . . . He went back to Esther.

'I've decided,' he said. 'I've decided what shall happen to my chief minister. He shall die on his own gallows! That's what shall happen to Haman.' [*Cheers*] 'And you, Esther, you and Mordecai shall have all his belongings.'

And that's what happened. And once a year, ever since, Jewish people have remembered how God did not allow their people to be destroyed, and the story of Esther is read in synagogues. And in that story, whenever they hear a certain name, the name of . . . the chief minister [*make them wait for his name*], they try to drown that name with noise, the name of wicked Haman! [*noise*] ◆

46

The Boyhood of Jesus

With the exception of one incident that is told in Luke 2.41–51, we know little of the boyhood of Jesus. We can, however, deduce something from what we know of that period from other sources. Jesus would have been instructed in the Old Testament by a local rabbi, he would have read Hebrew, and spoken Aramaic. He must also have picked up at least a smattering of Latin and Greek. This account by William Barclay describes some elements of school life in the time of Christ.

It is sometimes easy to think that people who lived in the past knew very little and were uneducated. We may sometimes think that even Jesus had very little schooling. That is not the case. He would have spoken the language Aramaic, but also have learnt to read Hebrew, the traditional language in which Jewish scriptures were written. And he would have been able to speak some Latin and Greek, which were languages widely spoken by the Romans who ruled the country in his time. And like any other boy of the time, he would have gone to school to be taught about the Jewish scriptures by a rabbi or teacher in Nazareth, the town in which he grew up.

◆

WHEN JESUS WAS a boy he went to the village school in Nazareth. A village teacher in Nazareth taught the boy who was going to have more impact on history than any other person ever had. We shall never know that teacher's name, but there *was* a teacher who taught the boy who was also the Son of God. When you are a teacher you never know what you are doing!

In those days at school, of course, they had not got any books ☞

because printing had not yet been invented. Everything had to be hand-written on rolls. The rolls (or scrolls) were tremendously expensive, and practically nobody could possess one for his own. Therefore if you were going to learn anything you had to learn it by heart. A Jewish boy when he went to school had to learn five things by heart.

First of all he had to learn the *Shema,* the basic creed of Judaism with which every synagogue service starts. *Shema* is the imperative of the Hebrew verb which means 'to hear'; it is the first word of the text: 'Hear, O Israel, the Lord thy God is one Lord and thou shalt love the Lord with all thy heart, with all thy soul, and with all thy strength.'

Secondly he would learn the *Hallel,* which means literally the 'Praise God'. The *Hallel* is Psalms 113–118, which are full of praise of God.

Thirdly he would learn Genesis 1–5, the story of creation and of how the world and the nations came into being.

Fourthly he would learn Leviticus 1–8. Leviticus is the law which tells of what is clean or unclean; what may be eaten and what may not be eaten; what may be touched and what may not be touched; and how a man can live a clean life according to the eyes of the Jewish law.

Fifthly the Jewish boy would be set to do something very interesting indeed. Although he had no books of his own, there were rolls and scrolls in the school, and he would be allowed to use these and to borrow them, and he was set searching for what was called a personal text. Now a personal text was a text which began with the first letter of his name and ended with the last letter of his name, and had all the other letters of his name included in between. For instance a text like this: 'A soft answer turns away wrath, but a grievous word ☞

stirs up anger', is a text for a boy called Abner, because it starts with 'A' and ends with 'R' and it has got B-N-E included in it.

The Jewis teacher sometimes gave his class a very interesting reward, which may have come to Jesus. In those days they had no paper and pencils, and they largely used slates and slate pencils or chalk, but sometimes the teacher would write the alphabet and he would write a sentence on a slate in a mixture of honey and flour; then he would take the slate and he would show it to a boy and say, 'What's that letter?' If the boy told him correctly, he was allowed to lick the letter off the slate. This is what the psalmist is referring to when he says, 'Thy words are sweeter to me than honey, and honey from the comb'. ◆

WILLIAM BARCLAY

47

Jesus the Carpenter

We know that Jesus was crucified when he was about thirty-three and that he spent only the last three years of his life engaged in his active ministry. So what did he do for the bulk of his life? Tradition has it that he worked as a carpenter in the business originally carried out by his earthly father, Joseph. This passage attempts to fill in some of the details of a carpenter's life in those days.

What did Jesus look like? Some pictures and films suggest that he was young with flowing golden hair and a small beard. He is not often thought of as being particularly muscular, but the fact that he could preach to vast multitudes (and presumably be clearly heard) points to great vocal power. So this suggests he had large lungs and therefore a big chest. One thing most people are agreed on is that he worked for much of his life as a carpenter. That too would have developed his physique. So Jesus was probably a strong man. This passage tells us something more about what it was like to be a carpenter in those days.

◆

ONE OF THE things that strikes anyone as being very surprising is why, if Jesus was to be the Saviour of the world, he spent thirty of these thirty-three years in Nazareth. Almost certainly what happened was that Joseph died when Jesus was still quite young, and Jesus had to take over the support of his mother and of his younger brothers and sisters, and of the home. Jesus once told a parable about a servant who was being praised. The master says to the servant: 'You've done well in a few things, I'm going to give a lot of things into your charge.' That was autobiography, for Jesus could never have become the ☞

Saviour of the world unless he had been the wage-earner of Nazareth. He had to do the little job well, before the big job could be given to him.

We slander Jesus a little when we call him a carpenter. He was what the Greeks call a *tekton,* and *tekton,* in Greek, meant a shipbuilder. And the tekton was much more than a carpenter. In many a Scottish village in the old days, and still to this day, there was a man with the minimum of tools, perhaps just a couple of chisels, and a hammer and a saw, and a set-square, and with this he would build you a house, or build you a bridge, or build you a coffin, or build you a table, or build you a chair. He would do anything – a craftsman in whose hands metal and wood became plastic and obedient. That is what Jesus was.

There is a legend which tells us that he made the best ox-yokes in the whole of Galilee, and that people beat a track to the door of Jesus of Nazareth to buy the ox-yokes that he made. In those days they had trade signs and beside the trade signs they had claims, as it were, for what they were going to do. It was suggested that over Jesus' carpenter's shop there was a yoke, and above it there was the sentence: 'My yokes fit well'. Jesus was later to say: 'Come unto me all ye that labour or are heavy laden, and take my yoke upon you, for my yoke is easy.' Now that does not mean that it is light and no bother. It is 'easy' in the sense that a pair of shoes are easy or a coat is easy, well-fitting: 'My yokes fit well'.

This of course means that Jesus was a working man. He knew the awkward narky customer, he knew the man who wouldn't pay his bills, he knew the kind of day when the devil got into the wood and the chisel and the saw, and when nothing would go right. He had done a day's work. ◆

WILLIAM BARCLAY

48

So Who Was Jesus?

The first two of these descriptions of Jesus are written from a Christian stance; the third is by a Roman historian. Students might discuss their objectivity: 'How true do you think this is?' Other 'follow-up' questions could include: 'Is it possible to ignore the life (and/or teaching) of Jesus?'

Who was Jesus? How would you answer that question? Here are some possible answers.

◆

JESUS CHRIST WAS born in Bethlehem almost 2,000 years ago. During his first thirty years he shared the daily life and work of an ordinary home. For the next three years he went about healing sick and troubled people and teaching small groups in villages, in the fields and by the lakeside. He called twelve ordinary men to be his helpers. He had no money. He wrote no books. He commanded no army. He wielded no political power. During his ministry he never travelled more than 200 miles in any direction. He was executed by crucifixion at the age of thirty-three.

Yet over 900 million people throughout the world now worship him as God.

Jesus Christ taught by what he said and by what he did. He taught us to trust in God as a loving and merciful Father and to pray, in faith, to him for all our needs and in all our difficulties. He taught that we are infinitely precious, that we are children of God, share in his Spirit, and should be patient with one another in love, understanding, respect and forgiveness.

He taught us to live in a spirit of thankfulness to God for all his ☞

gifts to us and always to be sensitive to the needs of others, especially those who are sick in mind or body and all who are lonely or distressed. He taught that our life in this world is a testing time and part of a greater and fuller life in God's eternal kingdom. He taught us to follow him in faith, simplicity and love and to try to live by his teaching.

Towards the end of his earthly life Jesus endured cruelty, suffering and death. God raised him from the dead to demonstrate to all men for all time that goodness will triumph over evil, justice over injustice, love over hate, life over death. Without the resurrection of Christ there would have been no Christian Church.

FROM A PAMPHLET AVAILABLE IN BATH ABBEY

Here is a man who was born in an obscure village, the child of a peasant woman. He worked in a carpenter's shop until he was thirty, and then for three years he was an itinerant preacher. He had no credentials but himself. While still a young man, the tide of popular opinion turned against him. His friends – the twelve men who had learned so much from him, and had promised him their enduring loyalty – ran away and left him. He went through a mockery of a trial. He was nailed upon a cross between two thieves; when he was dead, he was taken down and laid in a borrowed grave through the pity of a friend.

Yet I am well within the mark when I say that all the armies that ever marched, and all the parliaments that ever sat, and all the kings that ever reigned, put together, have not affected the life of man upon this earth as has this one solitary life.

ANON.

Now there was about this time Jesus, a wise man, if it be lawful to call him a man, for he was a doer of wonderful works, a teacher of such men as receive the truth with pleasure. He drew over to him both many of the Jews and many of the Gentiles. He was the Christ. And when Pilate, at the suggestion of the principal men amongst us, had condemned him to the cross, those that loved him at the first did not forsake him; for he appeared to them alive again at the third day; as the divine prophets had foretold these and 10,000 other wonderful things concerning him. And the tribe of Christians, so named after him, are not extinct at this day.

FLAVIUS JOSEPHUS (JEWISH HISTORIAN, BORN C. AD 37)

Whoever he was, he was the greatest of history's moral teachers. And the teaching is so far from being out of date that it has not yet been clearly understood. ◆

ANTHONY BURGESS

49

Dives and Lazarus

The parable told by Jesus about the rich man and Lazarus the beggar can be found in Luke 16.19–31. (This Lazarus should not be confused with Lazarus the brother of Martha and Mary). Nowhere in the Bible is the rich man actually called 'Dives', but that name is generally given to him from the Latin dives *meaning 'rich man'. Dives is often taken to represent gluttony, one of the seven deadly sins. In this parable Jesus was using a familiar folk tale and adapting it to a new purpose by adding an unfamiliar twist at the end. The story seems to have come originally from Egypt, but was popular among Jewish teachers of the time.*

The two people we are going to hear about today appear in a story told by Jesus. On the one hand, there is Lazarus, a poor man who made his living by begging. On the other hand, there is the rich man, Dives. Although they call each other 'brother' in the story, that is simply a way of greeting each other. They are not, in fact, related. As you listen to the story you will quickly see what messages Jesus was teaching when he first told it to his followers.

◆

AS IT FELL out upon a day,
Rich Dives he made a feast,
And he invited all his friends,
And gentry of the best.

Then Lazarus laid him down and down,
And down at Dives' door:
'Some meat, some drink, brother Dives,
Bestow upon the poor.'

'Thou art none of my brother, Lazarus,
That lies begging at my door;
No meat nor drink will I give thee,
Nor bestow upon the poor.'

Then Lazarus laid him down and down,
And down at Dives' wall:
'Some meat, some drink, brother Dives,
Or with hunger starve I shall.'

'Thou art none of my brother, Lazarus,
That lies begging at my wall;
No meat nor drink will I give thee,
But with hunger starve you shall.'

Then Lazarus laid him down and down,
And down at Dives' gate:
'Some meat, some drink, brother Dives,
For Jesus Christ his sake.'

'Thou art none of my brother, Lazarus,
That lies begging at my gate;
No meat nor drink will I give thee,
For Jesus Christ his sake.'

Then Dives sent out his merry men,
To whip poor Lazarus away;
They had no power to strike a stroke,
But flung their whips away.

Then Dives sent out his hungry dogs,
To bite him as he lay;
They had no power to bite at all,
But licked his sores away.

As it fell out upon a day,
Poor Lazarus sickened and died;

Then came two angels out of heaven
His soul therein to guide.

'Rise up, rise up, brother Lazarus,
And go along with me;
For you've a place prepared in heaven,
To sit on an angel's knee.'

As it fell out upon a day,
Rich Dives sickened and died;
Then came two serpents out of hell,
His soul therein to guide.

'Rise up, rise up, brother Dives,
And go with us to see
A dismal place, prepared in hell,
From which thou canst not flee.'

Then Dives looked up with his eyes,
And saw poor Lazarus blest:
'Give me one drop of water, brother Lazarus,
To quench my flaming thirst.

'Oh had I as many years to abide
As there are blades of grass,
Then there would be an end, but now
Hell's pains will ne'er be past.

'Oh was I now but alive again,
The space of one half hour!
Oh that I had my peace secure!
Then the devil should have no power.' ◆

ANON.

150

50

The Prophet Muhammad

This is a straightforward retelling of the call of the Prophet Muhammad, the great and last Prophet of Islam. In some circumstances it may be appropriate to add the phrase 'peace be upon him' after any mention of the Prophet's name, as is done by devout Muslims as a sign of respect to the one they honour above all others.

For Muslims – that is, the followers of the religion of Islam – the most important teacher of all time was the prophet Muhammad. This is the story of how he was called by God to start the religion of Islam.

◆

LONG AGO, IN what we in the West call the sixth century, in a city called Makka in the country of Arabia, there lived a young man called Muhammad.

Both his parents had died when he was six and he had been looked after first by his grandfather and then by an uncle. They were not wealthy: indeed, they were quite poor and Muhammad was not taught either to read or write. And yet, when he was much older, Muhammad was to give to the world a great book; a book that God was to give to him: the Holy Qur'an. But let's go back to when he was twenty . . .

At this time, Muhammad was working for his uncle who was a trader in the city of Makka – buying and selling things. And because Muhammad never tried to swindle their customers by overcharging them or cheating on the weight of something, he became known as Al-Amin, which means 'the Trustworthy'. And that became his nickname. ☞

One morning, his uncle sent for him. A wealthy widow called Khadija (who also lived in Makka) was looking for a young man to travel with (and care for) all her camels which she sent to other cities, carrying the things that she was buying and selling.

Now Muhammad's uncle would have liked his nephew to stay and work for him but, as he said, 'Business isn't so good. And Khadija needs someone to help in *her* business. It's best if you work for her. If she'll give you the job, that is.'

So Muhammad went to her house. 'I'm looking,' she said, 'for an honest man who will take charge of my business. Your uncle has recommended you. Would you be interested in the job?'

Muhammad thought about it for a time and then said yes. They talked about what he would have to do and soon everything was settled.

'I hear they call you Al-Amin. I hope that means you really are trustworthy.' Muhammad blushed, and said he hoped he would not let her down.

Muhammad worked hard and honestly and Khadija's business began to do even better. She was very pleased with him. In fact, she grew to like him very much – until one day she sent him a message. It was a proposal of marriage.

The wedding took place and it proved to be a long and happy marriage.

Muhammad knew he was a fortunate man: he was happy, he was lucky. Even so, there were times when he felt almost suffocated with work and business, with buying and selling things. At times like this he wanted to feel close to God, so he would walk out of the city of Makka, north to some hills, the hills of Hira – and especially to one particular cave, high up in ☞

the mountains. There he could be alone and there he could think. And as he watched the beauty of the twilight and the stars and the moon, there in the cave of Hira, Muhammad knew the greatness of God.

He began to spend more and more of his time at the cave, praying and thinking. Sometimes he stayed there for several days and Khadija would send him food.

Now one particular night, when Muhammad was in the cave, he heard a voice. And then, there in front of him, was a holy spirit, an angel. Muhammad looked in silence and wonder.

'Recite,' said the angel.

'What should I recite?' asked Muhammad. This happened three times and then the angel spoke again.

'Recite, in the name of God who made man from a drop of blood. Recite in the name of God.'

Muhammad repeated the words until he knew them by heart. Suddenly, the angel was gone and once again he was alone.

Quickly he made his way back down the mountainside to Makka and to Khadija.

When he got home, he told her all that had happened. 'Praise God,' she said.

Khadija had no doubt that Muhammad had been chosen to be a messenger for God, someone who would bring God's teaching to all the people. But Muhammad was doubtful.

Months passed. Many times Muhammad went back to the cave – and saw nothing. Then, ten months later, the angel appeared again. 'Warn the people. Tell them to praise God and to give up their wicked ways and turn from all that is wrong . . .'

And after that, the angel appeared often to Muhammad, giving him many more messages that he was to repeat to his family, to his friends and to those people of Makka who would listen to what he had to tell them. And Muhammad taught them the message of the angel: that there is only one God, whose name is God (or, in Arabic, Allah).

And from then on, Muhammad was called the Prophet or God's Messenger; indeed he truly was Al-Amin, the Trustworthy. And all that the angel told him was written down in a book which is called the Holy Qur'an. ◆

51

The Medieval Hitchhiker

*Margery Kempe (born about 1373) deserves to be more widely known.
A mystic, she was the daughter of the Mayor of King's Lynn. Her book,*
The Book of Margery Kempe *(which she dictated, being illiterate), is a
narrative of her spiritual journey through life in the course of which she
travelled to Italy, Jerusalem, Spain and Germany.*

*It was after her marriage that she experienced her profound religious
conversion. Her subsequent religious enthusiasm was sometimes a trial
to her husband and to those around her. She was given to copious
weeping at moments of extreme joy and devotion. Her autobiography is
one of the earliest books by a woman and certainly one of the earliest
autobiographies by a woman written in the English language.*

Margery Kempe was 'different'. She lived in King's Lynn
(then known as Bishop's Lynn) around the year 1400 – that is,
nearly 600 years ago. She was the daughter of the town's
mayor. She enjoyed her wealth and being considered an
important person in the town. After she married, she had
fourteen children!

At that time, women were expected to do little more than
serve their husbands in the home and in bed – but Margery
Kempe also ran a brewery. She continued to show off in fine
clothes around town and had a reputation for being an eager
lover!

Then, one day, she became highly religious. She denied all
sexual relations to her husband, and started going to church
several times a day. She had many rows with the bishops of
her day, usually because she thought they were not holy
enough.

In those days, married women were not allowed to travel on ☞

their own, but that did not stop Margery Kempe. She made a pilgrimage to the Holy Land, on her own, hitch-hiking her way right across Europe to Jerusalem to see the places where Jesus lived and was crucified. On her return, she visited other holy places in England (including York) and Spain.

Later, she became one of the first people to write their autobiography in the English language. She was also one of the first women to write a book in English. For many years, her book was 'lost', with only some of the more devout passages surviving in Cambridge University Library. Then the complete book was rediscovered in 1934. Here are some passages from it.

◆

Her belief in heaven

One night, as this creature lay in bed with her husband, she heard a melodious sound so sweet and delectable that she thought she had been in paradise. And immediately she jumped out of bed and said, 'Alas that ever I sinned! It is full merry in heaven.' This melody was so sweet that it surpassed all the melody that might be heard in this world, without any comparison, and it caused this creature when she afterwards heard any mirth or melody to shed very plentiful and abundant tears of high devotion, with great sobbings and sighings for the bliss of heaven, not fearing the shames and contempt of this wretched world. And ever after her being drawn towards God in this way, she kept in mind the joy and the melody that there was in heaven, so much so that she could not very well restrain herself from speaking of it. For when she was in company with any people she would often say, 'It is full merry in heaven!'

An accident in church

It so happened one Friday before Whitsun Eve, as this creature was in the church of St Margaret at Norwich, hearing mass, she heard a great and dreadful noise. She was greatly dismayed, very much fearing public opinion, which said God should take vengeance upon her. She knelt there, holding her head down, and with her book in her hand, praying to our Lord Christ Jesus for grace and for mercy. Suddenly – from the highest part of the church vault, from under the base of the rafter – there fell down on her head and on her back a stone which weighed three pounds, and a short end of a beam weighing six pounds, so that she thought her back was broken in pieces, and she was afraid that she would be dead in a little while. Soon after she cried, 'Jesus, mercy,' and immediately her pain was gone.

A good man called John of Wereham, seeing this marvel and supposing that she had been severely injured, came and pulled her by the sleeve and said, 'How are you feeling, ma'am?

This creature – entirely well and in one piece – thanked him for his kindness, all the time marvelling and greatly amazed that she now felt no pain and had felt so much a little before. Nor did she fell any pain for twelve weeks afterwards. Then the spirit of God said to her soul, 'Take this for a great miracle, and if people will not believe this, I shall work a great many more.'

Travelling to Jerusalem

On the way to Jerusalem, Margery Kempe's prayers and often noisy weeping annoyed the people she was travelling with – including a priest. One morning, on board the ship on which they were sailing, her companions played a trick on her.

When it was time to make their beds they locked up her bedclothes, and a priest who was in her party took a sheet ☛

away from this creature, and said it was his. She took God to witness that it was her sheet. Then the priest swore a great oath, by the book in his hand, that she was as false as she might be, and despised her and severely rebuked her.

And so she had great and continual tribulation until she came to Jerusalem. And before she arrived there, she said to them that she supposed they were annoyed with her, 'I pray you, sirs, be in charity with me, for I am in charity with you, and forgive me if I have annoyed you along the way. And if any of you have in any way trespassed against me, God forgive you for it, as I do.'

And so they went on into the Holy Land until they could see Jerusalem. And when this creature saw Jerusalem – she was riding on an ass – she thanked God with all her heart, praying him for his mercy that, just as he had brought her to see this earthly city of Jerusalem, he would grant her grace to see the blissful city of Jerusalem above, the city of heaven. Our Lord Jesus Christ, answering her thought, granted her her desire. ◆

MARGERY KEMPE

52

Mary Slessor, Missionary

Nowadays the role of the missionary is sometimes suspect. While it is thought admirable to work abroad in underdeveloped countries as a doctor or nurse, to do so as a religious missionary is not always so acceptable. This is partly the result, of course, of the insensitivity of previous generations of missionaries who have trampled over local cultures and beliefs with scant regard for those whom they were 'helping'. Some missionaries have also been guilty of the 'no bandages without belief' syndrome. Nevertheless, there have been many dedicated religious workers who have brought only good to the countries in which they have worked. Mary Slessor (1848–1915) was a Scottish missionary, born in Dundee, who worked in a factory from childhood but who felt she was being called to be a missionary. She was accepted by the Presbyterian Church as a missionary and went to Calabar, Nigeria, where she spent many years working among the inhabitants of that religion.

What is it that makes someone feel so determined to leave everything they have in this country and to work abroad in one of the poorer countries of the world? And what gifts or qualifications do you need to have in order to do such work? The answer is that anyone can help, provided that they have the determination and ambition. This is the story of a Scottish girl, Mary Slessor, who went to work in Africa. David Livingstone, who is mentioned in the passage, was another Scottish missionary and also a famous explorer in Africa.

◆

MARY SLESSOR WAS a factory girl in Dundee. From the age of fourteen she worked all day at a weaving machine to support her mother and family. However, for as long as she could remember she had wanted to be a missionary in the Calabar region of Nigeria. That was where her church, which ☞

had links also with Jamaica, had founded a mission. For it was from Calabar that years before many of the people had been taken to be slaves in Jamaica. Now that they were free, they thought of their homeland.

The death of David Livingstone in 1873 stirred many young people to work in Africa. Encouraged by her mother, Mary applied to go to Calabar and was accepted.

The region in which she was to spend the rest of her life was as hot, damp and unhealthy as anywhere in the world. She found that the people, women as well as men, were often drunk and violent. A chief would have many wives, as well as slaves: at his death his wives and slaves were slaughtered and buried with him. When anyone died for any other reason than old age, other people, often from another tribe, could be suspected of causing the death by witchcraft. Anyone suspected of witchcraft was forced to undergo ordeal by boiling oil or by poison. If the suspect's arm blistered when the boiling oil was poured on, this was proof of guilt, and the person was promptly executed. Or if, after drinking poisonous beans crushed in water, the suspect died, this too was proof of guilt.

They also believed that to have twins was a sign of evil. So whenever twins were born they were crushed alive into earthenware pots and put out into the forest to die. As soon as Mary heard that twins had been born, she rushed out and brought them into her own home for protection, until it became a refuge for unwanted babies. However, on one occasion relatives actually broke into the house and killed a boy twin.

This was hardly a place for a woman as frail as Mary. After a tornado had destroyed her house when she had been in Calabar six years, she became so ill that people thought she ☞

would not survive the sea voyage back to Britain. But she did survive, and returned to her work in Calabar.

The people came to trust her and to accept her advice. 'Run, Ma! Run,' they shouted when they wanted her to come and help. One day there was danger of a fight breaking out between two tribes. The chiefs of both sides, accompanied by their men armed with swords and spears and guns, sat under coloured umbrellas and argued for a day and a night. All the time Mary sat there at her knitting, listening and putting in a word when she thought things might be getting out of hand. Then at last, they all got up and parted in peace.

When the British government took over responsibility for the area, Mary was asked to be a judge of the district court. She dealt with people charged with murder, branding slaves with red-hot irons, rioting, assault, robbery. Often, if the crime was small, she punished the offender with a clip on the ear. And she did the same to any of the local chiefs who sat with her if they did not keep quiet.

Mary was often ill and in pain, but she refused to return to Scotland even when Britain went to war against Germany in 1914. She died in Africa, surrounded by some of the girls whom she had rescued as babies. ◆

EILEEN DUNLOP AND ANTONY KAMM

53

Edith Cavell, Nurse

Edith Cavell (1865–1915) was an English nurse who found herself in Belgium when it was overrun by the Germans early in the First World War. She remained in Brussels to nurse the wounded of both sides and helped over 200 Allied soldiers to escape into neutral Holland. When this activity was discovered she was put on trial and shot by the Germans. Her statue in St Martin's Lane, London, carries her own words: 'Patriotism is not enough. I must have no hatred or bitterness towards anyone.'

Edith Cavell was an English nurse who was working in Belgium when the First World War started in 1914. Soon after the start of the war Belgium was overrun by the Germans, but Edith Cavell stayed there to nurse the wounded of both sides. She ran a hospital that she had started there and one of her helpers was another nurse called Millicent White.

◆

LATE ON NOVEMBER 1st 1914 Sister Millicent White, one of Edith's nurses, was standing in the room across the corridor from Edith's office. She was reading a copy of *The Times*. Although it was over two weeks old and therefore very out of date, it was very precious. People in Brussels were not supposed to read about the fighting – especially from a newspaper produced in England. Copies were very hard to get; the paper normally sold for one penny, but Edith had paid £5 for it.

Sister White quickly hid the paper when she heard a knock at the door. Marie let in three men. Sister White thought perhaps they were German policemen, until she noticed that two of ☞

them were very poorly dressed. Marie went into Edith's office and soon came back to take the three men in to see her. A few minutes later the well-dressed man, Herman Capiau, left very hurriedly.

Shortly afterwards Edith came to find Sister White. 'This is Colonel Boger and Sergeant Meakin,' she said. 'They have both been wounded. You will look after them, won't you, and give them a meal? And you will see that they have some beer?' Sister White took them to the house next door, gave them food, and bandaged up their wounds.

The two men were members of the 1st Cheshire Regiment. Heavily outnumbered at Mons, the British army had quickly retreated westwards. Many soldiers and regiments lost touch with each other, and rapidly found themselves trapped in areas full of German soldiers. Colonel Boger had injuries to his hand, his side, and his right foot. Sergeant Meakin had been hit on the head by a spent bullet, and by a piece of shrapnel rebounding off a tree. Both had been captured, and taken to a field hospital; but they had managed to escape, and were given shelter by Albert Libiez, a Mons lawyer, who became a leading figure in the Resistance movement. Boger had now grown a beard, and was wearing a black hat and floppy tie like many Belgians of the time, while Meakin had disguised himself as a labourer, and was wearing shoulder pads to make him look like a hunchback.

Both men hoped to escape to England by way of Brussels and Holland; however, the Germans had declared that any British soldiers who did not surrender, and anyone who helped them, would be shot. Boger's foot injury was very bad, and it seemed likely that he might die unless he got urgent medical help. He and Meakin were brought to Brussels and it was Madame Depage who had suggested that Edith might help.

Boger and Meakin stayed at the clinic for two weeks. Gradually Edith began to fear that the house was being watched, so she arranged for them to be taken to another house in the city from where Boger, who was still very lame, was to travel to the Dutch coast on a coal barge, while Meakin would travel by land to meet him. Although deserted by his guide, Meakin managed to get to England, but Boger was captured and became a prisoner for most of the war . . .

Edith and the clinic became part of an organised Resistance movement. We shall never know exactly how many men passed through her hands, but the total may be 400 or even many more. Some stayed several weeks, others only a day or two.

Eventually, however, the Germans became aware of what was going on and started to watch the hospital closely. Edith Cavell was arrested and found guilty by the Germans of helping the enemy – which, of course, from their point of view was true.

Many people, on both sides of the war, were shocked when the German court announced her punishment was execution by firing squad.

Edith remained completely controlled when she heard the news. The priest asked if she would like the British chaplain in Brussels to be with her at her execution. 'Oh no,' she replied, 'Mr Gahan isn't used to things like that.' But she did agree to see him that evening. She was not allowed any other visitors.

Mr Gahan, dreadfully shocked at the sentence, arrived at the jail at 8.30 in the evening. 'She is a fine character,' the German warder told him. He went in to see her. 'All anxieties were set to rest in a moment,' he recalled. 'There she stood, her bright, gentle, cheerful self, as always, quietly smiling, calm and ☞

collected, even cheerful. She gave me a kind and grateful welcome.'

They took communion, prayed and said the hymn 'Abide with Me'. They talked a little. 'I have no fear,' she said, 'I have seen death so often that it is not strange to me. Life has always been hurried. This time of rest [in prison] has been a great mercy. Everyone here has been very kind. This I would say, standing as I do in view of God and eternity, I realise that patriotism is not enough. I must have no hatred or bitterness towards anyone.' She asked how she could be sure of going to heaven. Mr Gahan reminded her of the thief on the cross whom Jesus had forgiven with the words, 'Today you shall be with me in Paradise'. 'We shall always remember you as a heroine and as a martyr,' he told her. 'Think of me only as a nurse who tried to do her duty,' she replied. ◆

NIGEL RICHARDSON

54

Jean Goss and the Sadist

Jean Goss, a Frenchman, found himself in the army at the start of the Second World War. He became a committed Christian and later a pacifist. This anecdote illustrates the power of non-violence.

This is a true story about a Frenchman who was taken prisoner by the Germans during the Second World War. It shows that it is possible to overcome violence and cruelty by non-violence.

◆

JEAN GOSS WAS born in 1920, and the outbreak of war saw him in the French army. In 1940 he experienced a profound revelation of the reality of Christ, which transformed his life. Shortly after, he became a prisoner of war. His experience of Christ led him to realise that Christ's love knew no boundaries or limits and was the mainspring of all his actions. We are limited by our weakness, but must set no bounds on our love if we would follow him.

In the camp there was a sadistic SS guard. When the French prisoners came in, wearied from their day's work, he would take one of them on one side and beat him unmercifully for the sheer pleasure of causing pain. This was too much for Jean. One evening as they were lined up, he stepped out of line, marched up to this guard, and said 'Since you like beating people up, beat me up today.' 'What makes you think I wouldn't, Frenchy?' said the man threateningly. 'Your conscience.' 'Conscience. What conscience? I haven't got a conscience.' 'Oh, yes, you have,' said Jean. 'If you hadn't got a ☛

conscience you'd have hit me already. You haven't – and I don't think you're going to.' With that he turned his back on the tormentor and stepped again into line. When he turned round, this tough ruthless sadist was crying. He never beat up a prisoner again. ◆

JOHN FERGUSON

55

What I Have Lived For

This passage is more suitable for older students. It is taken from the autobiography of Bertrand Russell (1872–1970), the English philosopher, mathematician and controversial broadcaster. Besides his work in mathematics and logic, he was a radical thinker in many areas. He was fined and imprisoned for pacifism during the First World War, but a visit to the Soviet Union disillusioned him regarding communism. He abandoned his pacifist views in the Second World War, but later became a supporter of CND. During his lifetime, Bertrand Russell wrote his own obituary. Students might be encouraged to write their own 'obituaries', indicating what passions govern, or will have governed, their lives.

This passage was written by Bertrand Russell, a man who won many honours and distinctions during a lifetime spent mainly studying mathematics and logic. In this passage he describes three things that were most important to him during his life: three great 'passions'. As you listen, you might like to think what similar thoughts or ideals you might have by the end of your life.

◆

THREE PASSIONS, SIMPLE but overwhelmingly strong, have governed my life . . . the longing for love, the search for knowledge, and unbearable pity for the suffering of mankind. These passions like great winds have blown me hither and thither in a wayward course over a deep ocean of anguish, reaching to the very verge of despair. I have sought love, first, because it brings ecstasy, ecstasy so great that I would often have sacrificed all the rest of life for a few hours of this joy. I have sought it next because it relieves loneliness, that terrible loneliness in which one shivering consciousness looks over the ☞

rim of the world into the cold unfathomable lifeless abyss. I have sought it finally, because in the union of love I have seen, in a mystic miniature, the prefiguring vision of the heaven that saints and poets have imagined. This is what I sought, and though it might seem too good for human life, this is what at last I have found.

With equal passion I have sought knowledge. I have wished to understand the hearts of men; I have wished to know why the stars shine; I have tried to apprehend the Pythagorean power by which number holds sway above the flux. A little but not much I have achieved.

Love and knowledge, so far as they were possible, led upward toward the heavens. But always pity brought me back to earth. Echoes of cries of pain have reverberated in my heart. Children in famine, victims tortured by oppressors, helpless old people a hated burden to their sons, and the whole world of loneliness, poverty, and pain, make a mockery of what human life should be. I long to alleviate the evil, but I cannot. And I do suffer.

This has been my life. I have found it worth living, and would gladly live it again, if the chance were offered me. ◆

BERTRAND RUSSELL

56

The Cat With Three Lives

This is an account of the early life of the pop star Cat Stevens and of his subsequent conversion to Islam. It is offered as an illustration of how religion can bring a sense of purpose to someone's life and may be of comfort to those who think it would be embarrassing to 'catch religion'. Teachers of a certain age may be able to illustrate the passage with his recordings of Morning Has Broken, I Love My Dog *or* Matthew and Son.

In 1992, a journalist wrote in one of the posh Sunday papers about how he had to go to a church service for the first time in ages. 'I keep thinking,' he wrote, 'of a guy I met at the races who told me: I have just let the Lord Jesus into my heart. It just suddenly happened when I went into a church.' The journalist went on to describe how he didn't want that to happen to him. He said being in the church was like visiting a hospital and hoping not to catch the germs. 'Please let me not get God,' he had said to himself. 'It would ruin my reputation.'

This is the story of someone who was not afraid to risk his reputation by becoming religious.

◆

CAT STEVENS IS (or was) the Cat with three lives. Of course, you may not have heard of him. Twenty-five years ago, everyone had heard of this teenage pop star.

His real name was Steven Georgiou and he was born in London, in the West End where his Greek Cypriot father and Swedish mother ran a restaurant. As a boy, he was good at art and so, when he left school at the age of sixteen, he went to art ☞

college. In his first year there he found he liked music more and left. He began composing songs.

He was lucky. A record producer (who worked with Decca Records) used to eat in the family restaurant and he arranged for Steve or 'Cat' (a girlfriend had given the nickname) to record one of his songs called 'I Love My Dog'. Within weeks it was in the charts and Cat Stevens was on *Top of the Pops.* His next single, 'Matthew and Son', rapidly soared to number two. Cat toured Britain and Europe, always appearing on stage in his famous white suit. Then illness struck.

In was in 1968. Cat was drinking in a night club. Suddenly he slumped across the table. It proved to be a serious illness: tuberculosis. It took him a year to recover – and that year gave him time to think.

After his illness, he began a new life. Writing and performing songs again, but quieter, more thoughtful ones. He still made a lot of money but now he gave much of it away. When he gave a hundred thousand dollars to help poor children in Indochina, he said: 'I made the money on a world tour. It came easily. Now I want to share it around.'

Even so, he did not feel content. Things were going well for him. His records were in the charts; he was making money – but he knew something was missing. As he later said in a radio interview, 'Life was a game and an attempt to try to win it. But I had another side of my life which was bereft of guidance.' And in a song he wrote then (called 'To Be a Star'), he sang 'What is a star? It's somebody who is hungry for a bit of praise.'

Around this time, his brother David returned from a trip to Jerusalem with a copy of the Qur'an, the Muslim holy book. Cat was immediately interested. 'I always believed that there was a God but I didn't know how to direct myself to Him. The ☛

Qur'an puts you in touch with God.' And his interest in Islam meant a new way of life. He described it like this: 'I began to find I didn't like sitting next to people who were swearing. I didn't want to be with people who wasted their lives. I wanted to be with people who loved God.'

In 1978, Steven Georgiou, Cat Stevens, began his third life. He became a Muslim and took a new name, Yusuf Islam. Gone was the life of the teenage star, gone was the life of the grown-up singer. He had given away his 'pop' reputation and was now surrendering to what he felt really mattered. He married a Muslim and, with his wife and children, settled down in north London. He devoted much of his time to founding a school for Muslim children, where they could grow up learning the Muslim faith.

He believes it is wrong for people to worship idols and thinks it wrong for pop stars to encourage people to idolise them. In 1980, he gave away his musical instruments. As he said then, 'I will not be diverted from the true path.' He is someone who is not ashamed of having 'caught' religion. ◆

57

The Escape of the Dalai Lama

Tibet was an independent nation for more than 2,000 years, the last 300 of them under the rule of the Dalai Lamas. Then, in 1950, Chinese communists swept across the border and began a cruel and systematic extermination of the Tibetan culture and Buddhist religion. In 1959 the Dalai Lama and a band of his followers fled the country for safety in northern India, in order to preserve their culture and religion. In that year more than 400,000 Buddhists in Tibet were put to death.

Tibetans believe that when one Dalai Lama dies his soul is, some time afterwards, reincarnated in the person who will be his successor. The present Dalai Lama was born Lhamo Dhondup in 1935. He was brought from a country district to become the leader of his people while a young teenager, and was only fifteen when he had to cope with the invasion of his country by the Chinese. The passage describes his escape. It can be a starting point for discussion about the horror of religious persecution and also raises the question as to whether the Dalai Lama should have stayed in Tibet and been ruled by the communists or should have left his people to preserve what he believed in.

What is it like when you are put in charge of something? How well can you control a group of people? How do you know what is the right thing to say and the right course of action to take? Image that, at the age of fifteen, you were put in charge, not just of a small group of people (such as a classroom full of other pupils) – but of a whole country. How would you know what to do? And suppose that country was invaded, then what would you do? Those are some of the questions that faced a Buddhist known as the Dalai Lama who was ruler of a country called Tibet.

FAR AWAY, TO the north of India, are the Himalaya mountains. As you can perhaps imagine, it's a land of blue skies, swirling white snow and cloud. It's sometimes called the 'Roof of the World'. But beyond these mountains is a country called Tibet.

For hundreds of years, little has changed in the streets of Lhasa, its capital city. Above all, the people are peace-loving. They follow the teachings of a man called the Buddha; they are in fact Buddhists.

Some Buddhist men become monks. They wear red or yellow robes and give up all the luxuries of life to live very simply.

For hundreds of years, Tibet was ruled by the 'Dalai Lamas'. These men were also Buddhist monks. Or rather, the Dalai Lama *is* a Buddhist monk because the last Dalai Lama is still alive and lives in India. (The word 'Lama' means teacher or leader and the word 'Dalai' means ocean, so his name suggests that his knowledge, his wisdom, is as wide and as deep as the ocean.)

By the time the present Dalai Lama was just fifteen, he had already become ruler of Tibet. But in that year, 1949, the communist rulers of nextdoor China announced that they were going to make Tibet part of China. The Chinese army, they said, would march into Tibet. There was nothing the people of Tibet could do to stop them, and the following year the Chinese army *did* march into the Land of the Snows.

The young Dalai Lama knew that there was still much he had to learn about ruling a country. As he said, 'I know nothing about politics.' And there were many difficult decisions he had to make. Even so, he *was* the religious and political leader of his country – and his people trusted him to know what to do for the best.

For nine years he tried to make peace with the Chinese, but gradually they took over more and more of his country. They ☛

built roads so that their troops could move about easily. They destroyed many temples and monasteries where the monks lived. They tried to stop everyone from being Buddhists. But still the Dalai Lama hoped to save his people and their faith in Buddhism, and to do this without violence (because, like all Buddhists, he believed violence was always wrong).

However, many Tibetans were becoming impatient at the way the Chinese were interfering in their country. Some of them started to try to fight the Chinese.

The Chinese fought back. They moved more troops to Lhasa. Then the Tibetans began to fear the Chinese might kidnap or even kill the Dalai Lama. Indeed, many thought it best that he should leave the country. He wasn't sure. He didn't want to run away and leave his people to the Chinese army, but he understood their fears. However, many of his friends were certain that if he *was* killed or taken prisoner by the Chinese, that would be the end of Tibet. It would no longer be a separate country, but just part of China. But if he did escape, did 'run away', perhaps one day he could return and rule Tibet in peace again.

So that was his choice. What should he decide to do? Stay with his people and risk being killed? Or save himself in the hope that one day he might return? Not an easy choice.

He thought it over and over and reluctantly he decided he should leave the country.

The escape had, of course, to be kept a secret from the Chinese army. So he and a small group of his followers made their plans. First, they disguised themselves: no longer did they wear their red and yellow monks' robes, but instead wore the ordinary rough clothes of Tibetan soldiers.

The night they planned to escape, there was a sand storm. It ☞

could not have come at a better time, because it hid them from the Chinese.

Once they were outside the city, they found ponies waiting for them. The plan was going well. Quickly they mounted them. To the right were the lights of a Chinese camp. The Dalai Lama's companions were terrified the noise of the ponies' hooves on the stony path would alert the Chinese. But luckily, all the Chinese heard was the noise of the storm.

Their route led up through the mountains. The paths were narrow and difficult, and they often had to dismount and lead the ponies in the darkness. Then, in the morning, as the sun rose, a stranger suddenly appeared and offered the Dalai Lama a white horse on which to ride. They continued, more easily now, over the summit, down into a valley, and through villages where other people joined them. But news came that, back in Lhasa, the Chinese had destroyed the Dalai Lama's home and would be certain to kill him if they found him. Now he was certain he had to leave Tibet and make for the safety of India, even though the journey would take many days, perhaps even a month.

Then the weather worsened. Heavy snow bit into their faces. Then brilliant sunlight reflected off the snow and threatened to blind those without goggles. They slept at night in makeshift tents and, by day, struggled on, across hills and frozen desert plains. There were dust storms and later torrential rain. One night, the Dalai Lama's tent leaked so badly that he was forced to sit up shivering all night. He became very ill, but there could be no waiting till he got better. Reports of Chinese troops in the neighbourhood forced them to move on – until at last they crossed into India and safety.

Forty years have since gone by and still the peace-loving Dalai Lama has not been able to return to Tibet. ◆

58

Whatever You Do

Mother Teresa, an Albanian by birth, originally joined a teaching order of nuns, first in Dublin and later in India. The date 10 September 1946 was her 'day of decision'. She asked for permission to live outside the convent in India where she was teaching and to work in the Calcutta slums. In December 1948 she opened her first 'slum school' and later founded her Missionaries of Charity organisation which now operates world-wide. This meditation is based on Matthew 25.31–46, in which Jesus teaches that we glorify God by helping the needy.

A woman lay dying on a Calcutta pavement. She had been lying there for several days, without anyone taking any notice or helping her. Already her feet and hands were being eaten by the insects and rodents that lived in the street. Then a nun came by, a tiny woman dressed in a blue and white sari. Her name was Mother Teresa. She took the woman to a nearby hospital. She was told that the woman was too near death to be worth caring for. From that moment on, Mother Teresa started her work in Calcutta of helping the sick, the poor and the dying, attempting to give them as much comfort and dignity as possible. This passage was written by Mother Teresa and it is based on a teaching of Jesus: that it is his wish that we should give help to those in need. [*Students may repeat the response, printed in italics, after each verse. The meditation is printed here as originally written. Readers may well choose to replace the word 'Negro' in verse 8.*]

When I was hungry, you gave me to eat,
When I was thirsty, you gave me to drink,

Whatsoever you do to the least of my brothers,
    that you do unto me.
Now enter the house of my Father.

When I was homeless, you opened your doors,
When I was naked, you gave me your coat,

When I was weary, you helped me find rest,
When I was anxious, you calmed all my fears,

When I was little, you taught me to read,
When I lonely, you gave me your love,

When in a prison, you came to my cell,
When on a sick bed, you cared for my needs,

In a strange country, you made me at home,
Seeking employment, you found me a job,

Hurt in a battle, you bound up my wounds,
Searching for kindness, you held out your hand,

When I was Negro, or Chinese, or White,
Mocked and insulted you carried my cross,

When I was aged, you bothered to smile,
When I was restless, you listened and cared,

You saw me covered with spittle and blood,
You knew my features, though grimy with sweat,

When I was laughed at, you stood by my side,
When I was happy, you shared in my joy. ◆

MOTHER TERESA

59

The Stranger

Before reading this modern parable, it may be necessary to explain the meaning of the words 'partisan', 'resistance' and 'patriot'. Note that the parable contains two common factors of religious belief: faith based on personal experience as well as that based on argument. It may be apt to read the parable without explanation, then to discuss who the Stranger might be, and finally to read the passage a second time.

This is a modern parable about a country in wartime, when that country was being occupied by a foreign power. People in the country had joined together to form a resistance movement. As you listen to this story, which is called 'The Stranger', you might try to decide who you think the Stranger is.

◆

IN TIME OF war in an occupied country, a member of the resistance meets one night a stranger who deeply impresses him. They spend that night together in conversation. The Stranger tells the partisan that he is himself on the side of the resistance – indeed that he is in command of it, and urges the partisan to have faith in him no matter what happens. The partisan is utterly convinced at that meeting of the Stranger's sincerity and constancy and undertakes to trust him.

They never meet in conditions of intimacy again. But sometimes the Stranger is seen helping members of the resistance, and the partisan is grateful and says to his friends, 'He is on our side.'

Sometimes he is seen in the uniform of the police handing over patriots to the occupying power. On these occasions his friends murmur against him: but the partisan still says, 'He is ☛

on our side.' He still believes that, in spite of appearances, the Stranger did not deceive him. Sometimes he asks the Stranger for help and receives it. He is then thankful. Sometimes he asks and does not receive it. Then he says, 'The Stranger knows best.' Sometimes his friends, in exasperation, say, 'Well, what would he have to do for you to admit that you were wrong and that he is not on our side?' But the partisan refuses to answer. He will not consent to put the Stranger to the test. And sometimes his friends complain: 'Well, if that's what you mean by his being on our side, the sooner he goes over to the other side the better.'

The partisan of the parable does not allow anything to count decisively against the proposition 'The Stranger is on our side.' This is because he has committed himself to trust the Stranger. But he of course recognises that the Stranger's ambiguous behaviour does count against what he believes about him. It is precisely this situation which constitutes the trial of his faith. ◆

BASIL MITCHELL

60

An Old Jamaican Woman Thinks about the Hereafter

This simple West Indian poem needs little introduction. It might encourage students to write their own short passages to express their views about the hereafter.

What would I do forever in a big place, who
have lived all my life in a small island?
The same parish holds the cottage I was born in, all
my family, and the cool churchyard.
   I have looked
up at the stars from my front verandah and have been afraid
of their pathless distances. I have never flown
in the loud aircraft nor have I seen palaces,
so I would prefer not to be taken up high nor
rewarded with a large mansion.
   I would like
to remain half-drowsing through an evening light
watching bamboo trees sway and ruffle for a valley-wind,
to remember old times but not to live them again;
occasionally to have a good meal with no milk
nor honey for I don't like them, and now and then to walk
by the grey sea-beach with two old dogs and watch
men bring up their boats from the water.
   For all this,
for my hope of heaven, I am willing to forgive my debtors
and to love my neighbour . . .
   although the wretch throws stones
at my white rooster and makes too much noise in her damn
   backyard. ◆

A . L .   H E N D R I K S

THOUGHTS FOR A DAY

Lord, I shall be very busy this day.
  If I forget thee,
Do not thou forget me.

SIR JACOB ASTLEY, BEFORE THE BATTLE OF EDGEHILL;
A PRAYER WHICH MAY ALSO BE SAID BY TEACHERS MOST
MORNINGS

61

Bloody This and Bloody That

A reading to be used when an attack on the use of bad language seems necessary or apt. The passage probably needs no introduction, but time might be made for a brief follow-up discussion. Such a discussion might, with any luck, allow unfashionable views against the use of swear words to surface.

'GOOD MORNING. AND here's another bloody assembly.'

Well, at least you've never heard one start like that before – and that one word seems to have caught your attention.

It's an odd word, 'bloody'. It must get said millions of times a day – either in very upper-class voices like: 'You know me, Henry, I bloody told him . . . ', or in its real down-market use, as in 'Ee, bloody 'ell'. And there are people who seem unable to talk without using the word. For them, it's a matter of 'bloody this and bloody that and bloody everything . . . ' But what does it *mean*?

Once upon a time, it was a much stronger word than it is now. Indeed, some people think it was a really powerful oath meaning 'By our Lady', and those three words got run together to form 'bloody'. Our Lady is of course Mary, mother of Jesus. For many Christians, she is a very special person and not someone whose name you'd use to swear and cuss with.

Can you imagine what the word 'bloody' meant to her? Think of the first Good Friday when she stood by the cross, watching her Son being crucified. The soldiers hammering nails through his wrists (not palms, wrists), and later one of them plunging a ☞

spear into his side. A bloody crucifixion. That's when the word really does mean something. But the dictionaries simply say that 'bloody' is an adjective used to show strong dislike. Or anything to do with blood.

And blood is a good thing: it's precious. It's more valuable than money. The blood of Jesus or the blood of innocent victims of violence or war. Or our own blood. So easily lost; so easily infected. But life-giving. Vital.

And just as blood is important, so too is the word 'bloody'. Like blood itself, it needs using . . . carefully. ◆

62

Ten (or Eleven) Commandments

Once upon a time most twelve- or thirteen-year-olds would have been expected to know the Ten Commandments by heart. A sizeable number of those who knew them might also have understood them.

In recent times, more weight has been attached to Jesus' positive summary of 'the two great commandments' than to the Old Testament prohibitions:

> *'The first is, "Hear, O Israel: the Lord our God the Lord is one; and you shall love the Lord your God with all your heart, and with all your soul, and with all your mind, and with all your strength." The second is this, "You shall love your neighbour as yourself." There is no other Commandment greater than these.'*

However, as Jesus made clear on other occasions, he did not mean the Ten Commandments to be forgotten. This eighteenth-century summary is a perhaps more memorable version than the biblical one and one that (dare one suggest it?) might be learned by heart.

The second part of this passage is an unashamed attempt at moral uplift! (It will not be apt in every circumstance.)

Precisely how each of these two readings is introduced will depend very much on local circumstances.

The Ten Commandments (1731)

1 Have thou no other gods but me,
2 And to no image bow thy knee.
3 Take not the name of God in vain:
4 The sabbath day do not profane.
5 Honour thy father and mother too;
6 And see that thou no murder do.
7 Abstain from words and deeds unclean;
8 Nor steal, though thou art poor and mean.
9 Bear not false witness, shun that blot;
10 What is thy neighbour's covet not.

These laws, O Lord, write in my heart, that I,
May in thy faithful service live and die.

ANON.

Nowadays, some people seem to act as if the Ten Command-ments (you know, 'Thou shalt not kill', 'Thou shalt not commit adultery', and so on) are irrelevant, out of date. These people seem to think that the only commandment that really matters is the *eleventh* commandment: 'Thou shalt not get found out.' Or, as one boy wrote in an RE test, 'Thou shalt not *admit* adultery.'

Here's a better new commandment:

'Thou shalt not take other people for a ride.'

Not fashionable when plenty of people have as their motto, 'Never give a sucker an even break.' And you have to admit it's very tempting when the person in the shop makes a mistake and gives you change for a tenner instead of a fiver to take the extra money and run.

Or think of the scene from the film in which the fellow says to ☞

186

his girl, 'If you really love me, you'd do the one thing any girl would do for the bloke she loves.'

But he's trying to take her for a ride in more ways than one: that's not love, that's exploitation. Emotional blackmail. And yes, it can work the other way round when she starts muttering that if *he* doesn't want to, he must be a bit – well, you know.

It's tempting to exploit people in all sorts of ways. The state might not properly advertise the allowances some people are entitled to. The employer might not tell the worker all his rights. And you might be tempted to keep silent at a key moment. OK, so what? Except that, that way, the world becomes a harsher, harder place. A place where we all stand more chances of getting hurt. Jesus said, 'Love your neighbour.' If that commandment sounds too good to be true, try following this one, 'Thou shalt not take people for a ride.' And that way, you might not get taken for a ride yourself. ◆

63

When You're Told to Swim a Length

These lines were originally written as a song lyric and are probably more suited to the young pupils in the secondary-school age range. Pupils could make up their own rhythmic accompaniment to them. They are a kind of 'undirected prayer': a prayer to be used in moments of stress or loneliness. They have been phrased so that they may be used by followers of different faiths, or indeed those who follow no particular religion.

They can also serve as an introduction to (or explanation of) the nature of prayer if the leader points out that a Christian, for example, would address lines such as these to God or to Jesus when needing help and strength.

When you are at a new school there are often quite alarming and frightening moments when you are not sure what you are meant to do. There is no need to be ashamed of such feelings. Almost everyone experiences them at some time or other. Probably, in the past, you have felt moments of worry or even panic in situations like the following:

◆

When you're told to swim a length
And the deep end's rather deep;
When you think perhaps you'll drown
If the water pulls you down
As you haven't got the strength
And the deep end's rather deep –
Don't panic!
Don't panic!
Breathe deep,
Slowly;

And mumble in your mind,
'Give me help,
Make me brave,
Please do! Please do!'
Then you'll find,
Yes, you'll find
You have got the extra strength
And you don't mind
When you're told to swim a length
If the deep end's rather deep!

When there's something wrong at school
And you don't know what to do;
When you haven't understood
And your brain seems made of wood
When you fear you'll look a fool
As you don't know what to do –
Don't panic!
Don't panic!
Breathe deep,
Slowly;
And mumble in your mind,
'Give me help,
Make me brave,
Please do! Please do!'
Then you'll find,
Yes, you'll find
There's no chance you'll look a fool
And you don't mind
When there's something wrong at school
'Cause you know just what to do!

When it's dark upstairs at night
And you're really on your own;
When you're sure there's something there
That will trap you in its lair
And you wish there was a light
As you're really on your own –
   Don't panic!
   Don't panic!
   Breathe deep,
   Slowly;
   And mumble in your mind,
   'Give me help,
   Make me brave,
   Please do! Please do!'
   Then you'll find,
   Yes, you'll find
In the darkness there is light
And you don't mind
When it's dark upstairs at night
'Cause you're never on your own! ◆

64

The Hindu Way of Life

*There is an apocryphal tale told of the primary school pupil in a multi-
cultural school who invented his own religion. It forbade him to eat the
cabbage served regularly at school lunch.*

*Pupils are often curious, or occasionally suspicious, about the dietary
requirements of other religions. This passage may be used when it is
relevant to explain why, for example, Hindus do not eat beef. It also
goes on to explain other key aspects of the Hindu creed.*

Some people follow a diet because they think it will make
them healthier or more attractive in some particular way. In
many cases a healthy diet *does* make you much fitter. Other
people follow a diet for religious reasons. For example, Jewish
people do not eat pork. The passage you are now going to
hear is about the beliefs of Hindus and why they feel it is
wrong to eat meat – especially beef.

◆

FOR THE HINDU, everything – animal, bird or human – is
part of the Supreme One. Hindus also believe in reincarnation
– that after death, the soul is reborn in a new body. What kind
of body the soul is reborn into depends on how your life has
been lived. The more wicked and selfish you have been, the
more likely you are to be reborn as an animal or insect. But if
you try to live a good life, you can eventually escape being
reborn in this world, and return to the Supreme One.

This belief that the soul can be reborn into another form means
that Hindus see all life as sacred – it is all part of the Supreme
One. So, many Hindus believe that it is wrong to eat meat,
because that means killing animals. Instead, Hindus eat a wide ☛

range of fruits, pulses, grains and vegetables. Since vegetables are such an important part of their diet, Hindus are called vegetarians. The idea behind vegetarianism is respect for all life. Many Hindus believe that if there are other ways of getting food – such as gathering wild fruits, growing vegetables, keeping cows – then there is no need to kill animals.

In India, Hindus will never hurt or kill a cow. It is seen as a very special animal, and often called 'the mother' because it can produce so much for the family. The cow's milk can be made into yoghurt and curds, and it can also provide oil for cooking and for lamps. The cow's dung can be used as fuel, and its urine for building purposes. And it is the strength of the bull which pulls the plough, to help the family grow their crops. So to kill a cow just for its meat would be stupid. A dead cow cannot give as much as a living cow!

This has led to the cow being seen as a very important symbol of the care which must exist between humans and all other animals. In India, cows roam freely through the streets, and no Hindu will harm one. The great Indian leader, Mahatma Gandhi, said, 'In its finer or spiritual sense, the term cow-protection means the protection of every living creature.'

This duty to care for all living things is part of 'dharma'. Dharma is a very hard word to explain, but we can translate it as 'duty'. If we as human beings do our duty, then we create what is called good 'karma'. Karma is the result, the product, of what we do. Let's look at an example to see what dharma and karma mean.

A big hamburger firm recently advertised that they had served many billions of hamburgers. Now to Hindus that is a shameful boast. It means that millions of animals have been killed just to feed people. Just think of all that suffering! And it also means that in South America, the rain forests are slowly being destroyed to make bigger areas of grazing land for cattle, before they are slaughtered. In turn, this changes the very delicate balance of the earth's environment. Less rain, more poisonous fumes, not to mention all the wildlife that suffers or is lost too. So in the end, we are only hurting ourselves. Our lack of dharma, of duty towards other creatures, is bad karma – bad action.

For Hindus, this is very important. If someone dies with bad karma, then their souls will not be reborn in a human body. That person is more likely to be reborn as a lower creature, without the responsibilities that humans have.

So Hindus see humans as linked to all life. All life comes from the Supreme One, and is reborn time and time again, until the soul returns to the Supreme One. In the *Isa Upanishad*, an ancient and important book of Hinduism, it says: 'Everything in the Universe, living creatures or rocks or waters, belongs to the Lord. You shall therefore only take what is really necessary for yourself, your quota. You should not take anything else, because you know to whom it really belongs.' ◆

MARTIN PALMER AND ESTHER BISSET

65

Who Am I?

This is a short excerpt from A Portrait of the Artist as a Young Man. *It is hoped it will encourage wonder at the nature of God.*

You may have tried to imagine God. Who or what is God? This reading includes one boy's thoughts on that idea. They begin when he reads his full address, which he has written out in the front of one of his books.

◆

Stephen Dedalus
Class of Elements
Clongowes Wood College
Sallins
County Kildare
Ireland
Europe
The World
The Universe

He read the flyleaf from the bottom to the top till he came to his own name. That was he: and he read down the page again. What was after the universe? Nothing. But was there anything round the universe to show where it stopped before the nothing place began? It could not be a wall; but there could be a thin thin line there all round everything. It was very big to think about everything and everywhere. Only God could do that. He tried to think what a big thought that must be; but he could only think of God. God was God's name just as his name was Stephen. *Dieu* was the French for God and that was God's name too; and when anyone prayed to God and said *Dieu* then God knew at once that it was a French person that was praying. But, though there were different names for God in all the different languages in the world and God understood what all the people who prayed said in their different languages, still God remained always the same God and God's real name was God.

It pained him that he did not know where the universe ended. ◆

JAMES JOYCE

66

For God's Sake

Just as passage 61 ('Bloody This and Bloody That') may be used as an attack on crude language, so this passage may be used to draw attention to the thoughtless use of the name of God. What to some people is an everyday, almost meaningless, expression is to others (be they Christian, Muslim or followers of another religion) a form of blasphemy or at least a source of offence. (Some readers may prefer to omit the last sentence of this passage.)

WHICH WORD DO you think gets used most often as a swear word?

No, I don't think it's the one you're thinking of. I suspect it's the word 'God'. For many people, this is a very mild expression. 'Oh God, I don't know' they say – and they mean hardly anything at all. Other folk use it much more strongly – still as a swear word, but as an expression of anger or temper. And some people, who *do* believe in God, use his name almost as a curse – when they feel he's let them down in some way or other.

You've perhaps heard they're talking about changing, or even giving up, the law of blasphemy. Blasphemy means 'taking the name of God in vain' or denying the existence of God. Non-believers probably all think such a law is long out of date. And if you look at it logically, if you genuinely *don't* believe in God, it's difficult to see how you can take his name in vain. But that's the puzzling thing: if you *don't* believe in him, what use is his name as a swear word?

But to many other people, God is something, someone very special, very precious – and to hear his name being used ☛

196

casually, crudely, is just as upsetting as hearing someone slagging-off a person you love.

So if you're in the habit of using God's name carelessly, without thinking, just remember that the habit can be hurtful to those for whom his name is important. It can in fact be a kind of verbal aggro. (And if you do keep on using the word 'God' when you don't mean anything at all, how can you be sure it'll mean something the day you need it?) ◆

67

Sixes and Sevens

Just as passage 6 ('Christmas Mastermind') was an attempt to use an established television format to remind students of some of the basic facts about Christmas, so this script may be used to teach some of the salient and sometimes forgotten facts about the life of Jesus. Deliberately jokey in tone, it parodies a local radio phone-in competition. Martin is the studio host, and Adam Everyman is the distant contestant.

Obviously it will benefit from rehearsal before presentation to any group. In one or two places sound effects or 'radiophonic' sounds may be used to give realism. The use of a klaxon by Martin to indicate a wrong answer can also be effective.

Just how much do you know about Jesus? Supposing you had to take part in a radio phone-in competition, how well would you do?

◆

MARTIN: Hi, you're tuned to River Radio and yes, it's me, Martin Flood, making waves on the medium wave. Six minutes to the top of the hour and that means it's time for: Sixes and Sevens! Yes, Sixes and Sevens, your chance to show just what you know, and our caller on line number one is Adam Everyman – hi there –

ADAM: Hello, Martin.

MARTIN: Adam Everyman, that's an everyday sort of name – yes?

ADAM: That's what everyone says, Martin.

MARTIN: [*slightly put down*] Yes, well. [*Bright and breezy*] Adam, you don't mind if I call you Adam – you're not married to Eve by any chance?

ADAM: Eve who?

MARTIN: Eve. The garden of Eden. [*Pause*] Just my little joke, sorry about that. Say, Adam, you're ready to play Sixes and Sevens where you have to get six questions out of seven correct – or the seventh one (which is a real toughie) – to win one of our super prizes?

ADAM: I'm ready, Martin.

MARTIN: Well, let's spin the magic dial – and see what's today's subject. [*Sound effect*] And today's subject is Jesus Christ.

ADAM: Not an easy subject, Martin.

MARTIN: As you say, Adam. But here goes – seven questions on Jesus Christ. One, in which town did Jesus grow up? Was it Jerusalem, Bethlehem or Nazareth?

ADAM: Bethlehem. That was his home.

MARTIN: Wrong! No, that's where he was born. He grew up in Nazareth. Bad luck, Adam. Question two. What do we think his job was? Was he a priest, a doctor or [*slight, 'don't be daft' sort of laugh*] a carpenter?

ADAM: He was religious so he must have been a priest.

MARTIN: Wrong! He was a carpenter – or so we believe. Third question. Who ruled the country in which he lived? Was it the Americans, the Jews or the Romans?

ADAM: [*laughs*] You won't get me with that one. It wasn't the Americans . . .

MARTIN: So who was it?

ADAM: It was the Jews. It was their country.

MARTIN: Well, it was their country and they did have some powers, but the people with the real power were the ☞

Romans. They'd made it part of the Roman Empire – which wasn't popular with everyone. Next question. In which year was Jesus probably born? The year 1, the year 0 or the year 5 before Christ?

ADAM: [*confident*] Year 1. That's when we number the years from, Martin. From his birth.

MARTIN: Wrong! Nope – and there wasn't a year 0. No, we now think he was born some four or five years before the year we used to think he was born in. So he was probably born around the year 5 (or possibly 4) BC.

Question number five. About how old was he when he was killed on the cross? Thirty? Thirty-three? Or fifty-three?

ADAM: [*doubtful*] Thirty?

MARTIN: Wrong! Thirty-three. Question number six. What colour hair did he have? Was it blond, dark, or don't we know?

ADAM: This is a trick one, isn't it, Martin?

MARTIN: I'm not saying anything.

ADAM: Well, I've seen pictures of him with blond hair, but most people who live in that part of the world have black hair – so I'll say dark haired.

MARTIN: Wrong! The answer is, we don't know. Well, Adam, six wrong – but you can still win [*patronising laugh*] if you get number seven right. [*Still laughing*] OK, Adam Everyman?

ADAM: I don't know, Martin.

MARTIN: Well, here goes. Jesus was his first name – so was Christ his surname, his mother's name or his father's name? ☞

ADAM: It wasn't a name at all. It's a title. It means 'the one who will save us' – sort of 'the chosen one'.

MARTIN: Correct! [*Astonished*] Well, yes. Yes. You got the first six questions wrong. All of them. But, Adam Everyman, you knew the one that mattered, the seventh question – so if you stay on the line, we'll take your details and see about that prize. Meanwhile, this has been Sixes and Sevens with Martin Flood on Radio River. ◆

68

At *the* Name *of* Jesus

Few but the devout now pay much attention to the words of St Paul in his letter to the Philippians: 'At the name of Jesus every knee should bow'. However, there are Christians who believe that while just reverence is now properly given to the name of the prophet of Islam, the name of Jesus is regularly taken in vain. Like passage 66 (which attempted to rescue the name of God from thoughtless use), this reading attempts a similar rescue job on the name of Jesus Christ – so often used as an expletive. The two sections that follow may be used together or on separate occasions. They may usefully lead into a discussion of blasphemy and why it remains a serious matter to some people, despite the claims of others for artistic freedom.

Jesus

I wonder if you've ever had the bad experience of overhearing someone cursing a person you're fond of or even really keen on? Maybe they didn't know you could hear; maybe they didn't know how you felt – but all the same you heard them going on about 'that lousy little Tracey' or 'ruddy Harry So-and-so'. And yes, it can hurt when you hear a friend's name cursed, or maybe just laughed at.

Names are precious. One of the ways we get hurt is when people make fun of our names – when they take them in vain. But one special name gets taken in vain all the time. Whether it's shortened down to 'Jeez', or said in full – 'Jesus'.

To people who follow Jesus , his name is the most important name of all. It's so important that one of his early followers, the man we know as St Paul, said that 'at the name of Jesus, every knee should bow'. Even today, especially when they're in ☞

church, many Christians do bow their knee or at least their head when his name is mentioned.

Now the name of Jesus may mean nothing to you and you may not care a scrap about the feelings of those to whom he is important. So in that case it's up to you how you use his name. But if you care at all about other people's feelings, before you use his name thoughtlessly, you might just stop to think whom you might be offending. And to think who might overhear you – and that includes Jesus himself.

Christ

If I asked you which is the strongest swear word, there's a good chance you'll agree fairly quickly on one particular one. And it's one you can see on walls and overhear in streets (and doubtless in school corridors). But it's a word that's still heard on radio or television fairly rarely. Even these days, it's kept its power, its magic if you like, at least to a certain extent (even if a few people manage to include it in every other sentence).

But for some people there's an even stronger word – and yet you'll hear that word regularly used in plays and films (even comedy shows) and most of those watching will hardly notice it at all. They'll take it for granted that, as an expression of surprise or anger, you can say it quite openly in any pub, office, factory or even school – any day of the week.

The word is 'Christ'.

It's not a name. It's a title. In Greek it's Christos – which is Greek for a Hebrew word, the Messiah. The one who is anointed. The one who is special or chosen, set apart.

Now the word God is important enough, but why should the title 'Christ' be even more important? For Christians, the ☞

misuse of the word 'God' can be in bad taste. But (for them) the word 'Christ' has only one, very special, meaning. There is only one Christ – and abusing his title is to abuse the Special One they worship, the One they believe matters most to them. And that's why (for Christians) the use of 'Christ' as a swear word is more offensive than that four-letter word you may have first thought of – but which I'm not going to use in assembly. ◆

69

Splintered Messiah

This poem voices an opinion that has been prevalent since the time of Jesus himself. It is the feeling that Jesus was not the sort of leader (or king) that people would have chosen. Most people expect a leader to be powerful in an earthly sense. They certainly don't want a leader whose career apparently ends with a criminal's death on a cross. The poem might provoke discussion of what sort of Messiah pupils might be tempted to follow, or encourage them to write their own poems about their own true or false 'gods'.

If there was an election and Jesus was a candidate, would you vote for him? Is he the sort of leader who would win your vote? Or, put it another way: if Jesus were alive today and a friend of yours, would you take him with you to a party? This poem explains how Jesus can make people uncomfortable. Many people (the writer is saying) might be happier with another kind of leader or Christ.

◆

I don't want a splintered Messiah
in a sweat stained greasy grey robe
I want a new one
I couldn't take this one to parties
people would say who's your friend?
I'd give an embarrassed giggle and change the subject
If I took him home
I'd have to bandage his hands
The neighbours would think he's a football hooligan
I don't want his cross in the hall
it doesn't go with the wallpaper
I don't want him standing there

like a sad ballet dancer with holes in his tights
I want a different Messiah
streamlined and inoffensive
I want one from a catalogue
who's as quiet as a monastery
I want a package tour Messiah
not one who takes me to Golgotha
I want a King of Kings
with blow waves in his hair
I don't want the true Christ
I wanna false one. ◆

STEWART HENDERSON

70

The Long Silence

This modern Christian parable makes the point that Jesus was not simply a leader in his own time, but a leader for all time. During his life on earth, he suffered some of the forms of persecution and prejudice that we think of as exclusively 'modern' or contemporary.

Christians believe that one of the greatest things that Jesus did for them during his life on earth was to suffer just as they sometimes have to. For example, they believe that, during his life 2,000 years ago, he suffered from prejudice and cruelty in ways that are sadly all too common today.

So this story answers the charge that God (or Jesus) doesn't know what it's like to be human today. It begins in the far distant future, on the last day of all time . . .

♦

AT THE END of time, billions of people were scattered on a great plain before God's throne. Most shrank back from the brilliant light before them. But some groups near the front talked heatedly – not with cringing shame, but with belligerence.

'How can God judge us? How can he know about suffering?' snapped a pert young brunette. She ripped open a sleeve to reveal a tattooed number from a Nazi concentration camp. 'We endured terror . . . beatings . . . torture . . . death!'

In another group a black boy lowered his collar. 'What about this?' he demanded, showing an ugly rope burn. 'Lynched for no crime but being black! We have suffocated in slave ships, been wrenched from loved ones, toiled till only death gave release.'

In another group, a young girl stared with sullen eyes. On her forehead was the stamp 'illegitimate'. 'To endure my stigma,' she murmured, 'was beyond, beyond . . . ' and her voice trailed off, to be taken up by others.

Far out across the plain were hundreds of such groups. Each had a complaint against God for the evil and suffering he permitted in his world. How lucky God was to live in heaven where all was sweetness and light, where there was no weeping, no fear, no hunger, no hatred. Indeed, what *did* God know of what man had been forced to endure in this world? After all, God leads a pretty sheltered life, they said.

So each of these groups sent forth a leader, chosen because he had suffered the most. There was a Jew, a black, an untouchable from India, an illegitimate, a horribly deformed arthritic, a person from Hiroshima, and one from a Serbian slave camp. In the centre of the plain they consulted with each other. At last they were ready to present their case. It was quite simple. Before God would be qualified to be their judge, he must endure what they had endured. Their decision was that God should be sentenced to live on earth – as a *man!*

But, because he was God, they set certain safeguards to be sure that he could not use his divine powers to help himself: Let him be born a Jew. Let the legitimacy of his birth be doubted so that none will know who is really his father.

Give him a work so difficult that even his family will think he is out of his mind when he tries to do it.

Let him try to describe what no other man has ever seen, tasted, heard or smelled. Let him try to describe God to man.

Let him be betrayed by his dearest friends.

Let him be indicted to false charges, tried before a prejudiced ☛

jury, convicted by a cowardly judge.

At last, let him see what it means to be terribly alone, completely abandoned by every living thing.

Let him be tortured, and then let him die.

Let him die so that there can be no doubt that he died.

Let there be a great crowd to verify it.

As each leader announced his portion of the sentence, loud murmurs of approval went up from the great throng of people assembled. When the last had finished pronouncing sentence, there was a long silence.

Those who had spoken their judgement of God quietly departed.

No one uttered a word.

No one moved.

For suddenly all knew.

God had already served his sentence. ◆

A.T.L. ARMSTRONG

71

Meditation

Cardinal John Henry Newman (1801–90) was a Church of England clergyman who moved to the Roman Catholic Church in 1845. Non-believers may feel that his famous 'Meditation' is something of a 'cop-out' in that it superficially excuses God from helping those who pray to him. It is, say its critics, an example of Christianity promising 'pie in the sky'. However, that has not stopped it from comforting and encouraging many believers in periods of trial and tribulation, as well as in good times. Note that, although it is a form of prayer, it is not narrowly Christian.

Christians are sometimes asked, if God really loves them, then why do they have to suffer. Why doesn't everything go right for them? This meditation, or prayer, was written by a Christian clergyman to encourage other Christians at moments when they seem unsure of what they should do, or times when God does not seem to be helping them.

◆

GOD HAS CREATED me to do him some definite service. He has committed some work to me which he has not committed to another. I have my mission.

I may never know it in this world, but I shall be told it in the next. I am a link in the chain, a bond of connection between persons. He has not created me for nothing. I shall do good. I shall do his work. I shall be an angel of peace – a preacher of truth in my own place, if I do but keep his commandments.

Therefore will I trust him. Wherever, whatever I am, I can never be thrown away. If I am in sickness, my sickness may serve him; in perplexity, my perplexity may serve him; if I am ☛

in sorrow, my sorrow may serve him.

He does nothing in vain. He knows what he is about. He may take away my friends. He may throw me among strangers. He may make me feel desolate, make my spirits sink, hide my future from me . . . still . . . he knows what he is about. ◆

CARDINAL NEWMAN

72

I *Haven't Time*

This is part of a Christian prayer, based on one of the commonest of human excuses: 'I haven't time' or 'I didn't have time'. It may be taken as a reminder for the proper use of time.

(Note: Because it was written some years ago, this prayer may now sound sexist; users of this book might prefer to devise more up-to-date versions of the prayer that are nevertheless still 'timely'.)

Some people seem to have too much time. Unemployed people are often bored by long, empty days with nothing to do. Old people (and young people) sometimes complain of having nothing to do. But many of us don't seem to have enough time. Can you think when you last said, 'I haven't time'? This reading is a kind of prayer that says that we shouldn't waste time, that we should be thankful for all the time we do have, and that we should use our time wisely and for things and people that matter.

◆

I went out, Lord.
Men were coming out.
They were coming and going,
Walking and running.
Everything was rushing, cars, lorries, the street, the whole town.
Men were rushing not to waste time.
They were rushing after time,
To catch up with time,
To gain time.

Goodbye, sir, excuse me, I haven't time.
I'll come back, I can't wait, I haven't time.

I must end this letter – I haven't time.
I'd love to help you, but I haven't time.
I can't accept, having no time.
I can't think, I can't read, I'm swamped, I haven't time.
I'd like to pray, but I haven't time.

You understand, Lord, they simply haven't the time.
The child is playing, he hasn't time right now ... Later on ...
The schoolboy has his homework to do, he hasn't time ...
    Later on ...
The student has his courses, and so much work, he hasn't
    time ... Later on ...
The young man is at his sports, he hasn't time ... Later on ...
The young married man has his new house, he has to fix it up, he
    hasn't time ... Later on ...
The grandparents have their grandchildren, they haven't time ...
Later on ...
They are ill, they have their treatments, they haven't time ...
Later on ...
They are dying, they have no ...
Too late! ... They have no more time!

And so all men run after time, Lord.
They pass through life running – hurried, jostled, overburdened,
frantic, and they never get there. They haven't time.
In spite of all their efforts they're still short of time,
    of a great deal of time.
Lord, you must have made a mistake in your calculations.
There is a big mistake somewhere.
The hours are too short,
The days are too short,
Our lives are too short.

You who are beyond time, Lord, you smile to see us fighting it. ☞

And you know what you are doing.
You make no mistakes in your distribution of time to men.
You give each one time to do what you want him to do.

But we must not lose time
    waste time,
    kill time,
For time is a gift that you give us,
But a perishable gift,
A gift that does not keep. ◆

MICHEL QUOIST

73

Go *Placidly*

This passage, written over 300 years ago, is probably one of the best pieces of careers advice ever given. Though one paragraph assumes belief in God, it is not otherwise a 'confessional' reading and will be acceptable in almost all circumstances. Because it contains much good advice, it may be beneficial for pupils to hear it on more than one occasion or to be given time to think about it, section by section.

You may not think it when you first hear this passage, but it was written 300 years ago. It was discovered in an American church and is a piece of advice on how to live your life successfully and happily.

◆

GO PLACIDLY AMID the noise and haste, and remember what peace there may be in silence. As far as possible without surrender be on good terms with all persons. Speak your truth quietly and clearly; and listen to others, even the dull and ignorant; they too have their story.

Avoid loud and aggressive persons, they are vexations to the spirit. If you compare yourself with others, you may become vain and bitter; for always there will be greater and lesser persons than yourself. Enjoy your achievements as well as your plans.

Keep interested in your own career, however humble; it is a real possession in the changing fortunes of time. Exercise caution in your business affairs; for the world is full of trickery. But let this not blind you to what virtue there is; many persons strive for high ideals; and everywhere life is full of heroism. ☛

Be yourself. Especially do not feign affection. Neither be cynical about love; for in the face of all aridity and disenchantment it is perennial as the grass.

Take kindly the counsel of the years, gracefully surrendering the things of youth. Nurture strength of spirit to shield you in sudden misfortune. But do not distress yourself with imaginings. Many fears are born of fatigue and loneliness. Beyond a wholesome discipline, be gentle with yourself.

You are a child of the universe, no less than the trees and the stars; you have a right to be here. And whether or not it is clear to you, no doubt the universe is unfolding as it should.

Therefore be at peace with God, whatever you conceive him to be, and whatever your labours and aspirations, in the noisy confusion of life keep peace with your soul.

Be careful; strive to be happy. With all its sham, drudgery and broken dreams, it is still a beautiful world. ◆

DATED 1692 AND FOUND IN A CHURCH IN
BALTIMORE IN AMERICA

74

No Man Is an Island

This passage emphasises the need to care for our neighbours and acknowledges the fact that we are dependent on them for our own well-being. Obviously it would be helpful if the listening group were able to hear a recording of Pete Seeger's song 'Little Boxes'.

How independent are you? Can you manage without other people? Are you, in fact, your own separate little island who has no need of anyone else – or do you need lots of other people around you all the time?

◆

THERE IS A song by Pete Seeger called 'Little Boxes'. The 'little boxes' are houses, and his song is about the way we all like the privacy of our own little homes and how we try to preserve our own secret way of life, in our own little box. But, at the same time, we don't want to be different. We're keen to conform, to fit into what we believe is a sociably acceptable pattern.

'An Englishman's home is his castle' is an old and valued saying and, while there's nothing wrong in privacy and security, it's not an entirely happy attitude.

Centuries ago, before the Industrial Revolution, we *all* lived in villages, villages where there was no privacy at all, and where everyone knew everyone else's business. You might think this absolute hell, but village life didn't just mean gossip and people intruding – it also meant friendliness and true neighbourliness. And if you lived on your own, you wouldn't have to be afraid of being ill and there being no one to look after you. Everyone was part of a community; you had close neighbours who would help ☛

217

you when need be. They had to, for survival. 'You help with my harvest, and I'll help with yours.'

But now it's different. Many of us live in large towns – towns that are getting more and more like concrete jungles. Deserts of glass and concrete where, despite the thousands of people rushing about, there's no one with whom to share a joke or a problem when you're on your own.

It's difficult to preserve the balance between being independent, of having your own little castle, your own little box; and, on the other hand, of being part of a community. But if the world is going to be a better place for our existence in it, we've got to care about the rest of the community, not just for what we'll get out of it, but because we must be ready to sacrifice a little time for the needs of others. Caring for people isn't just nodding sympathetically after a television documentary about down-and-outs, or giving a quid to a charity. That's part of it; but it's also about being prepared to put ourselves out to help someone else. It's going out of our way to help the old invalid; it's being an audience for the tedious old bore who always tells the same long-winded story . . . It's remembering that despite the haste, the tempo of modern living, life is nothing without people.

Yes, it's possible to be a busybody, but it's also easy to try to wriggle out of the knowledge that we are involved with the people around us. As a poet called John Donne once wrote, 'No man is an island, entire of itself; every man is a piece of the continent, a part of the main.' And he went on, 'Any man's death diminishes me, because I am involved in mankind; and therefore never send to know for whom the bell tolls, it tolls for thee.'

So by answering its call to our conscience, we'll not only brighten someone else's life, but also our own. For whatever we may proudly think, we need each other as John Donne said, 'No man is an island.' ◆

75

By All That's Wonderful

This passage aims to introduce pupils to one of the more famous poems by William Wordsworth and, more importantly, to encourage a sense of wonder at the world around us. It may be helpful if listeners have the first few lines of his sonnet 'Composed Upon Westminster Bridge' in front of them as the passage is read.

(Note: It is, of course, a requirement of the National Curriculum that students should be introduced to the poetry of previous centuries.)

Almost 200 years ago there lived a poet called William Wordsworth. Some people think that he always wrote poems about the natural world. It's true he wrote a famous poem about daffodils and another about a rainbow, but he also wrote one about the city of London – in particular, Westminster Bridge which crosses the River Thames.

◆

IMAGINE THE SCENE – it could be taking place about now. London, the River Thames. One of the bridges that cross the river. There's a stream of commuters pouring into the city. Two men are talking on their way to work.

'You know, I was just thinking . . . ' says one of them.

'Yes?' says the other.

'Well, this view. You know, there are few finer sights on earth.

'You what? London? The city? You've got to be joking. There are *far* finer sights on earth than this.'

'No, no.' The first man is quite serious. 'You must admit, you'd have to be pretty dull of soul to pass by a sight so majestic as this. ☛

'Majestic?'

'Yes, I think it is. In the morning light.'

'What is?'

'The ships, the tower, that theatre, the dome of St Paul's Cathedral. They're just as beautiful, in their own way, just as mysterious, if you like, as – well, a mountain view.'

And so on.

Now it's easy to say that maybe the city *did* look pretty fine in the morning light when (almost 200 years ago) the poet William Wordsworth wrote this poem 'Composed upon Westminster Bridge':

Earth has not anything to show more fair:
Dull would he be of soul who could pass by
A sight so touching in its majesty:
This City now doth, like a garment, wear
The beauty of the morning; silent, bare,
Ships, towers, domes, theatres, and temples lie
Open unto the fields, and to the sky;
All bright and glittering in the smokeless air.

Yes, perhaps it did look all right *then,* says the cynic – but look at it now. Concrete and tower blocks.

But that isn't the point. Wordsworth wasn't just being the starry-eyed romantic, painting a pretty picture. What he was saying is as relevant today as when he wrote it: that our souls or imaginations would be pretty dull, not to say dead, if we aren't awake to beauty; to seeing beauty in the most unpromising sights. Like the London skyline.

It's the same with the wonders of nature – a rainbow for example. As Wordsworth also wrote:

My heart leaps up when I behold
A rainbow in the sky.

A small child is excited by a rainbow. He or she can 'wonder' at it, and see the mystery of the rainbow. The adult is all too inclined to say, 'Ah yes, rainbow. Must be rain about.' Or, as a scientist might say, 'It's just refraction and reflection of light during precipitation.'

Scientifically speaking, it was useful that we resolved the puzzle of what causes a rainbow, of what makes us see the seven colours of the spectrum; but even when we've solved the puzzle, we should still try to see the mystery, the wonder of the rainbow.

Mercifully, we do all preserve some element of romance within our souls. If we're in the middle of a crowd of strangers and a person we love walks into the room, we feel uplifted. We don't psychoanalyse away our elation, we don't say to ourselves, 'Ah yes, the geometrical arrangement of that person's facial characteristics is once again emotionally and aesthetically satisfying.' We respond to the mystery of love, and we greet them – perhaps even embrace them.

We should not condemn the scientific approach; it's right in its place, but the human being also has a capacity to wonder, to respond to the mysterious and the beautiful. And if we concentrate only on being sensible, down-to-earth, then we're denying the spiritual element that's in us all, and we're not being fully human. ◆

76

Ley Lines

In 1925 a Hereford photographer and brewer's representative called Alfred Watkins published a book called The Old Straight Track. *In it he developed his theory that Britain is criss-crossed by a series of 'straight tracks' or 'leys'. He noticed that the beacon hills, mounds, earthworks, moats and old churches built on pagan sites seemed to fall into straight lines across the whole country. His investigations convinced him that Britain was covered with a vast network of these 'ley lines'. Although traces of this network can indeed be found all over the country, the principle behind it remains a mystery. Was the purpose secular or religious? Did the lines (as some have suggested) possess some strange magnetic force?*

This passage is not intended to encourage belief in something that may be akin to UFOs, but instead (like the previous reading) to encourage a sense of wonder; to help young people to open their minds to new ideas; indeed, to accept the mysterious – or religious – element in life.

Do you believe only in what can be proved scientifically or are you prepared to make a leap of faith and say you believe in something that can't be proven? Or do you just like to keep an open mind?

◆

YOU MAY REMEMBER when the newspapers and television got excited about crop circles: patterns that appeared overnight in fields or corn, with some people claiming they were made by flying saucers and others saying they were practical jokes.

Well, every so often television and the newspapers also get interested in 'ley lines'. These are supposed to be mysterious lines of force that criss-cross the British Isles. Many of them ☛

lead to so-called 'magical' places such as Stonehenge and Avebury and so on.

No one really knows for certain whether these lines are just a fantasy, or whether they are simply ancient roads or even threads of magnetic power in the earth that we don't know about but that our ancestors understood. According to some people, our ancestors even used them to transport heavy objects about the countryside – like shifting those heavy blocks of stone from the Prescelly mountains in Wales to build Stonehenge.

And there are the related mysteries. What exactly was the point of building a calendar the size of Stonehenge up there on the top of Salisbury Plain? And why (for example) are so many of our ancient churches built in straight lines, so that if you get an Ordnance Survey map you'll find that the same straight line goes through a whole succession of churches, all built on traditional holy sites?

It is of course possible to say it's all just a fluke and that Stonehenge has no real meaning and that ley lines are just the imaginings of a few cranks. One day we may unravel or disprove such mysteries, but (until then) it could be important to keep open minds about them.

This isn't just so that we don't miss making some useful scientific discovery in the future, it's much more immediate than that. It's because a readiness to be aware of mystery, to appreciate what's wonderful in the world around us, does extend and enrich our daily lives. Even the most basic sort of mystery, like whether there's a Loch Ness Monster or not, adds interest to life.

But more importantly, being ready to appreciate *beauty*, to wonder at the mysterious, makes life much more agreeable, more satisfying. If only we will allow ourselves to see the ☞

mystery behind the obvious, just as much in a rainbow or the view across the River Thames as in the face of the people we love, then we will be uplifted, freed from a merely earthbound viewpoint. We shall experience moments that are literally divine. But it's more even than this. By being ready to say 'yes' to the mysterious element in life, we will discover we possess powers we never knew we had, we will experience things we can't even dream of. Or at least we might.

If you pride yourself on being rational, logical, a humanist who rejects any idea of faith in what can't be proved, if you deny the mysterious like that, then you're denying a part of your being.

For whether we like it or not, there is a part of each one of us that is creative, imaginative, capable of wonder. And by closing our minds to the mysterious, we're not being fully human. ◆

77

God's Handwriting

Charles Kingsley (1819–75) was a Church of England clergyman and one of the founders of the Christian socialist movement. He is probably best known for his historical romances (e.g. Hereward the Wake*) and also for* The Water Babies. *This passage is taken from a work called* 'True Words for Brave Men' *published in 1848. It is idealistic in tone, but none the worse for that. It may be particularly suitable for older students in urban schools.*

We each have our own idea of what the word 'beauty' means. For some it will be another person, for others it will be a picture, and for yet others it will be a landscape. This is a passage that reminds us that we are all made happier and are enriched in all sorts of ways if only we notice and appreciate the beauty that is around us. And if we're in a situation in which there seems to be little beauty, then we must seek it out wherever possible.

❖

THOSE WHO LIVE in towns should carefully remember this, for their own sakes, for their wives' sakes, for their children's sakes. *Never lose an opportunity of seeing something beautiful.* Beauty is God's handwriting – a wayside sacrament; welcome it in every fair face, every fair sky, every fair flower, and thank for it *Him,* the fountain of all loveliness, and drink it in, simply and earnestly, with all your eyes; it is a charmed draught, a cup of blessing. Therefore I said that picture-galleries should be the townsman's paradise of refreshment. Of course, if he can get the real air, the real trees, even for an hour, let him take it in God's name; but how many a man who ☛

cannot spare time for a daily country walk, may well slip into the National Gallery, or any other collection of pictures, for ten minutes. *That* garden, at least, flowers as gaily in winter as in summer. Those noble faces on the wall are never disfigured by grief or passion. There, in the space of a single room, the townsman may take his country walk – a walk beneath mountain peaks, blushing sunsets, with broad woodlands spreading out below it; a walk through green meadows, under cool mellow shades, and overhanging rocks, by rushing brooks, where he watches and watches till he seems to *hear* the foam whisper, and to *see* the fishes leap; and his hard-worn heart wanders out free, beyond the grim city-world of stone and iron, smoky chimneys, and roaring wheels, into the world of beautiful things – *the world which shall be hereafter* – ay, which shall be! Believe it, toil-worn worker, in spite of thy foul alley, thy crowded lodging, thy grimed clothing, thy ill-fed children, thy thin, pale wife – believe it, thou too, and thine, will some day have *your* share of beauty. ◆

CHARLES KINGSLEY

78

Miracles

Walt Whitman (1819–92) is sometimes said to be the first distinctively American poet. His poem 'Miracles' is a celebration of the miracle of life and the miracle of creation. It is another reading that is designed to encourage a sense of wonder at the world around us.

You don't have to believe in God to appreciate the miracle of life. Either by the design of God or by some scientific accident, conditions were right at one distant moment in the past to allow the creation of our universe. And that led to the creation of our own world and subsequently to life on earth as we know it. Whether you believe it to be the work of God or a scientific accident, it is still a 'miracle' that it happened. And if only we look around us and realise what we are seeing, then (according to this poem) we can appreciate that miracle.

◆

Why, who makes such a miracle?
As to me I know of nothing else but miracles,
Whether I walk the streets of Manhattan,
Or dart my sight over the roofs of houses toward the sky,
Or wade with naked feet along the beach just in the edge of
   the water,
Or stand under trees in the woods,
Or talk by day with anyone I love, or sleep in the bed at night
   with anyone I love.
Or sit at table at dinner with the rest,
Or look at strangers opposite me riding in the car,
Or watch honey-bees busy around the hive of a summer fore-
   noon,

☞

Or animals feeding in the fields,
Or birds, or the wonderfulness of insects in the air,
Or the wonderfulness of the sundown, or of stars shining so
    quiet and bright,
Or the exquisite delicate thin curve of the new moon in
    spring;
These with the rest, one and all, are to me miracles,
The whole referring, yet each distinct and in its place.

To me every hour of the light and dark is a miracle,
Every cubic inch of space is a miracle,
Every square yard of the surface of the earth is spread with the
    same,
Every foot of the interior swarms with the same.

To me the sea is a continual miracle,
The fishes that swim – the rocks – the motion of the waves –
    the ships with men in them,
What stranger miracles are there? ◆

WALT WHITMAN

79

My Dear Wormwood . . .

The book The Screwtape Letters, *written by C. S. Lewis, was first published in 1942 and became an immediate religious bestseller. The author's subtitle ('Letters from a Senior to a Junior Devil') explain the letters' format. Screwtape is responsible for training his nephew, young Wormwood, in the art of tempting human beings and winning them for 'Our Father below'. This particular letter shows how the devil might tempt new Christians by emphasising the mundane elements in church life.*

(Note: It was Martin Luther who said, 'The best way to drive out the Devil . . . is to jeer and flout him, for he cannot bear scorn.')

You may or may not believe in a devil who tempts us to do wrong, but certainly *something* tempts us from time to time to do wrong. Today's reading suggests how the devil (if he exists) might try to tempt people who become church-goers. It's a letter written by a very senior devil called Screwtape to a much younger devil, Wormwood. Wormwood has the responsibility of tempting one particular human being – but this person has just become a Christian. This failure by Wormwood to keep his human being (or 'patient') out of church has of course infuriated Screwtape. Screwtape is now suggesting to Wormwood how he can still win the human being's soul for 'Our Father below' which is, of course, the name the devils use to refer to their boss, the devil himself. Remember, when the devils talk about 'the enemy', they mean God.

◆

My Dear Wormwood,

I note with grave displeasure that your patient has become a Christian. Do not indulge the hope that you will escape the usual penalties; indeed, in your better moments, I trust you would hardly even wish to do so. In the meantime we must make the best of the situation. There is no need to despair; hundreds of these adult converts have been reclaimed after a brief sojourn in the Enemy's camp and are now with us. All the *habits* of the patient, both mental and bodily, are still in our favour.

One of our great allies at present is the Church itself. Do not misunderstand me. I do not mean the Church as we see her spread out through all time and space and rooted in eternity, terrible as an army with banners. That, I confess, is a spectacle which makes our boldest tempters uneasy. But fortunately it is quite invisible to these humans. All your patient sees is the half-finished, sham Gothic erection on the new building estate. When he goes inside, he sees the local grocer with rather an oily expression on his face bustling up to offer him one shiny little book containing a liturgy which neither of them understands, and one shabby little book containing corrupt texts of a number of religious lyrics, mostly bad, and in very small print. When he gets to his pew and looks round him he sees just that selection of his neighbours whom he has hitherto avoided. You want to lean pretty heavily on those neighbours. Make his mind flit to and fro between an expression like 'the body of Christ' and the actual faces in the new pew. It matters very little, of course, what kind of people that next pew really contains. You may know one of them to be a great warrior on the Enemy's side. No matter. Your patient, thanks to Our Father below, is a fool. Provided that any of those neighbours sing out of tune, or have boots that squeak, or double chins, or odd clothes, the patient will quite ☛

easily believe that their religion must therefore be somehow ridiculous . . .

Work hard, then, on the disappointment or anticlimax which is certainly coming to the patient during his first few weeks as a churchman. The Enemy allows this disappointment to occur on the threshold of every human endeavour. It occurs when the boy who has been enchanted in the nursery by *Stories from the Odyssey* buckles down to really learning Greek. It occurs when lovers have got married and begin the real task of learning to live together. In every department of life it marks the transition from dreaming aspiration to laborious doing. The Enemy takes this risk because He has a curious fantasy of making all these disgusting little human vermin into what He calls His 'free' lovers and servants . . .

Desiring their freedom, He therefore refuses to carry them, by their mere affections and habits, to any of the goals which He sets before them: He leaves them to 'do it on their own'. And there lies our opportunity. But also, remember, there lies our danger. If once they get through this initial dryness successfully, they become much less dependent on emotion and therefore much harder to tempt.

Your affectionate uncle

Screwtape ◆

C. S. LEWIS

80

Heaven – A Tourist's Guide

*Christians sometimes say that the point about heaven is that we cannot
know what it will be like. If we did know how wonderful it will be, they
say, then we might be tempted to speed up our departure for that new
life! But the Bible does include several mentions of heaven – as this
'travel guide' indicates. (Pupils might be given the opportunity to
describe what their heaven will be like).*

Just what do you think heaven will be like? When the time
comes for you to make your journey there, what will you
need to keep in mind? For example, will you need a passport
and permission to enter? Do you know your exact departure
time and what customs declaration you might have to make?
What accommodation will you expect to find?

◆

A Guide for Travellers

Passports

Persons seeking entry will not be permitted past the gates
without having proper credentials and having their names
registered with the ruling Authority:

> But nothing that is impure will enter the city, nor anyone
> who does shameful things or tells lies. Only those whose
> names are written in the Lamb's book of living will enter the
> city (Revelation 21.27).

Departure times

The exact date of departure has not been announced. Travellers are advised to be prepared to leave at short notice:

> Jesus said to them, 'The times and occasions are set by my Father's own authority, and it is not for you to know when they will be (Acts 1.7).

Tickets

Your ticket is a written pledge that guarantees your journey. It should be claimed and its promises kept firmly in mind:

> I am telling you the truth: whoever hears my word and believes in him who sent me has eternal life. He will not be judged, but has already passed from death to life (John 5.24).

Customs

Only one declaration is required while going through customs:

> And now I want to remind you, my brothers, of the Good News which I preached to you, which you received, and on which your faith stands firm . . . . I passed on to you what I received, which is of the greatest importance: that Christ died for our sins, as written in the Scriptures; that he was buried and that he was raised to life three days later, as written in the Scriptures (1 Corinthians 15.1, 3–4).

Immigration

All passengers are classified as immigrants, since they are taking up permanent residence in a new country:

> Instead, it was a better country they longed for, the heavenly country. And so God is not ashamed for them to call him ☞

their God, because he has prepared a city for them (Hebrews 11.16).

Luggage

No luggage whatsoever can be taken:

> What did we bring into the world? Nothing! What can we take out of the world? Nothing! (Timothy 6.7).

Air passage

Travellers going directly by air are advised to watch daily for indications of imminent departure:

> Then we who are living at that time will be gathered up along with them in the clouds to meet the Lord in the air. And so we will always be with the Lord (1 Thessalonians 4.17).

Vaccination and inoculation

Injections are not needed as diseases are unknown at the destination:

> He will wipe away all tears from their eyes. There will be no more death, no more grief or crying or pain. The old things have disappeared (Revelation 21.4).

Accommodation

Arrangements for first-class accommodation have been made in advance:

> There are many rooms in my Father's house, and I am going to prepare a place for you. I would not tell you this if it were not so (John 14.2). ◆

FROM THE WINCHESTER CHURCHMAN

LOVE THY NEIGHBOUR AS THYSELF

We must love one another or die.

W. H. AUDEN

81

The Typical Teenager

This passage was a summary by the education editor of The
Independent *of a report called 'Young People in 1986' published by the
Health Education Authority, Schools Health Education Unit of Exeter
University. Although it was published some years ago, one suspects that
not much has changed. Because it is about themselves, teenagers should
find it a source of immediate interest!*

*Some listeners may feel justifiably smug after hearing it; others should
(with luck) feel uncomfortable. It is offered as a way of making young
people in the middle and upper part of the secondary school think about
how they use their time.*

What do you think a typical teenager is like? Is he or she a
drinking, smoking layabout or a hardworking studious
person who always does the washing-up at home? And how
do you measure up against the average? Are you better or
worse? This is a report of a survey conducted a little while ago
to find out what makes 'a typical teenager'.

◆

THE TYPICAL BRITISH teenager is a clean, hardworking
non-smoker, who spends generously on presents but is
somewhat prone to headaches and ill-at-ease with the opposite
sex, according to research published not so long ago.

The teenage day starts with cereal, a glance at a popular
newspaper and possibly a morning paper-round. It continues
with regular attention to teeth and smelly armpits but an
excessive intake of alcohol, sugar and fat; winds down with the
minimum of homework and reading, and lots of goggling at
television; and concludes with a bedtime between 10 and ☞

11pm, after abortive attempts to extract information about sex from parents.

This picture emerges from a survey of 18,000 adolescents, who were questioned on a school day during term-time.

In all age groups (except girls aged eleven to twelve), well over a third had done no homework the previous night, usually, they claimed, because it was not set. Even among fifth-year boys (fifteen to sixteen), only one in four spent more than an hour on their homework. Girls were more conscientious or maybe slower: more than one in three of the fifth-years did home-work for more than an hour.

In all age groups, far more time is spent watching television. The majority of boys and girls watched television after school for at least two hours. Some 18 per cent of first-year boys (aged eleven and twelve) watched for five hours or more. Remarkably, 20 per cent in this age group – and at least 15 per cent in the others – found further time to watch videos. One in three of the first-year boys also played computer games, although fewer than one in five of their girl classmates did so.

The majority of boys had not read at all the previous evening. One in four first-year girls, however, had spent at least an hour reading and, until the fourth year, the majority did some reading. But, for both sexes, the amount of reading tended to decline with age.

Barely 10 per cent in any age group had spent money on books in the previous month. The older boys and girls were four times more likely to spend money on alcohol and cigarettes.

The intake of alcohol – most commonly at home and so presumably with parental approval – is perhaps the most worrying aspect of the survey. Even among first-year girls, the ☞

lightest drinkers, one in three had had an alcoholic drink in the previous week.

Counting a pint of shandy as a unit of alcohol, the majority of first-year boys had consumed at least one unit, while one in three fifth-year boys and one in five girls had consumed more than seven. In the fifth-year, 7 per cent of the boys were already imbibing more than 21 units a week – the level at which adult men are warned that they may be in danger of alcoholism.

Smoking was slightly less of a problem. In all age groups, three in four had not smoked in the previous week and the majority had never started, or had smoked only once or twice. Most smoked lightly – even among fifth-year boys, under 6 per cent had smoked more than 66 cigarettes in the previous week.

The majority who did smoke already wanted to give up.

Other findings from the survey include:

- The majority bath or shower at least twice a week – about a quarter of fourth and fifth-year girls do so once a day.
- The majority think parents should be their main source of information about sex – but the majority also find this is not the case. About one in three fall back on friends for information, reluctantly in most cases.
- More than 95 per cent claim to help at home with gardening or housework. The majority of boys did so only sometimes, but about 30 per cent of girls, against under 20 per cent of boys, helped every day. Some 29 per cent of first-year boys and 47 per cent of fifth-years had a paid term-time job. ◆

PETER WILBY

82

Eating People Is Wrong

It was the writer Anthony Burgess who said, 'The need to hold the whole of humanity together in a bond of tolerance, forgiveness and charity is an aspiration which requires no belief in God to justify it.' Or, to put it another way, you do not need to believe in God to see that it is wrong to use people thoughtlessly or cruelly and to treat them as objects that serve our needs.

In their revue, At the Drop of a Hat, *Michael Flanders and Donald Swann included a sketch called 'The Reluctant Cannibal'. Part sung, part spoken, it effectively conveyed the message that 'eating people is wrong'. The opening part of that sketch forms the first part of this passage.*

For the beginning of this reading I want you to imagine a distant desert island, inhabited only by cannibals . . .

◆

SEATED ONE DAY at the tom-tom, I heard a welcome shout from the kitchen.

'Come and get it. Roast leg of Insurance Salesman.'

A chorus of yums ran round the table.

'Yum, Yum, Yummmmmm . . . '

Except for Junior who pushed away his shell, got up from his log and said: 'I don't want any part of it.'

'What! Why not?'

'I don't eat people. Ugh! I won't eat people. I don't eat people. Agh! Eating people is wrong.'

'It's wrong? People have always eaten people. What else is there to eat? If the Ju-Ju had meant us *not* to eat people, he wouldn't have made us of meat!'

We perhaps laugh at that scene because the idea is quite horribly revolting. Almost everyone must be offended by the idea of cannibalism, of eating people. But is that passage just about cannibalism? Do we not 'eat' people' in all sorts of other ways? Consuming them, using them for what we can get out of them? Hoping to get something for very little?

It is, in fact, very easy to use people, not as a cannibal uses his captives as food, but as stepping stones towards an object in our lives – without stopping to consider the feelings of the people we're treading on.

You may have had a daydream in which you see the world as a film or play in which you are the main character and everyone else is merely taking part in your film or in your story. Sitting in a school bus, you drive past crowds of people in the street and you start to imagine they have no life or purpose other than to act as incidents in your life. Would they exist if you didn't?

Of course they would. The moment any of us falls into the trap of believing others to be less important than ourselves, then we are well on the way to breaking one of the most important rules of life, 'Love thy neighbour as thyself'. That is a Christian commandment, but you don't need to be a Christian to realise that unless we are tolerant of each other, unless we forgive each other and care about each other, then the whole business of everyday life becomes very, very much more difficult and unpleasant.

'Don't eat people! Eating people is wrong!' Of course – a ridiculous idea, but we can 'use' other people in a way that's just as cruel and as unpleasant. It may be using our age and size to bully a much younger child into giving us a bit of chocolate. It may be trying to talk a person of the opposite sex into doing something to please us without really thinking of their ☞

emotions and of what they want. It may be by landing someone else in some form of trouble at school – simply to keep us out of trouble.

If we treat people as objects in our lives, then we're denying their dignity as human beings – and then we're not so far removed from the cannibal who thinks that other people exist simply to provide his supper. ◆

83

Universal Declaration of Human Rights

*The United Nations is an association of states for international peace,
security and co-operation. It was established in 1945 as a successor to the
League of Nations and has played a role in many areas such as refugee
aid, disaster relief and in policing warring states. In December 1948 the
General Assembly of the UN adopted the Universal Declaration of
Human Rights. This passage is an extract from it.*

*It is, of course, a sad reminder that all is not for the best in our multi-
cultural world. For example, a report by Amnesty International in 1991
showed that human rights abuses continue and (in that year) worsened
in 141 countries. In over 100 countries prisoners were tortured or ill-
treated. In twenty-nine countries thousands of people disappeared or
were executed outside the law.*

*Human Rights Day is 10 December, commemorating the adoption of
the Universal Declaration by the General Assembly.*

*It is not suggested that all twenty-one articles be read as one passage.
They may be read over a series of assemblies or even just one used as the
basis for discussion in a given assembly. They are printed here as a
resource for the assembly leader to use as appropriate. Consequently, it is
not possible to give an introduction that will be suitable in all situations.*

*Students might be asked to think of ways in which certain articles
have been or are being broken. They might also be encouraged to bring
cuttings from newspapers and magazines to make a montage illustrating
the different concepts expressed in the articles.*

Article 1 All human beings are born free and equal in dignity
and rights. They are endowed with reason and conscience and
should act towards one another in a spirit of brotherhood.

Article 2 Everyone is entitled to all the rights and freedoms set
forth in this Declaration, without distinction of any kind, such
as race, colour, sex, language, religion, political or other opinion,
national or social origin, property, birth or other status.

Article 3 Everyone has the right to life, liberty and security of person.

Article 4 No one shall be held in slavery or servitude; slavery and the slave trade shall be prohibited in all their forms.

Article 5 No one shall be subjected to torture or to cruel, inhuman or degrading treatment or punishment.

Article 6 Everyone has the right to recognition everywhere as a person before the law.

Article 7 All are equal before the law and are entitled without any discrimination to equal protection of the law.

Article 8 Everyone has the right to an effective remedy by the competent national tribunals for acts violating the fundamental rights granted him by the constitution or by law.

Article 9 No one shall be subjected to arbitrary arrest, detention or exile.

Article 10 Everyone is entitled in full equality to a fair and public hearing by an independent and impartial tribunal, in the determination of his rights and obligations and of any criminal charge against him.

Article 11 Everyone charged with a penal offence has the right to be presumed innocent until proved guilty according to law in a public trial at which he has had all the guarantees necessary for his defence.

Article 12 No one shall be subjected to arbitrary interference with his privacy, family, home or correspondence, nor to attacks upon his honour and reputation.

Article 13 Everyone has the right to freedom of movement and residence within the borders of each state. Everyone has ☞

the right to leave any country, including his own, and to return to his country.

Article 14 Everyone has the right to seek and enjoy in other countries asylum from persecution.

Article 15 Everyone has the right to a nationality. No one shall be arbitrarily deprived of his nationality nor denied the right to change his nationality.

Article 16 Men and women of full age, without any limitation due to race, nationality or religion, have the right to marry and to found a family. They are entitled to equal rights as to marriage, during marriage and at its dissolution. Marriage shall be entered into only with free and full consent of the intending spouses.

Article 17 Everyone has the right to own property alone as well as in association with others. No one shall be arbitrarily deprived of his property.

Article 18 Everyone has the right to freedom of thought, conscience and religion; this right includes freedom to change his religion or belief, and freedom, either alone or in community with others and in public or private, to manifest his religion or belief in teaching, practice, worship and observance.

Article 19 Everyone has the right to freedom of opinion and expression; this right includes freedom to hold opinions without interference and to seek, receive and impart information and ideas through any media and regardless of frontiers.

Article 20 Everyone has the right to freedom of peaceful assembly and association. No one may be compelled to belong to an association.

Article 21 Everyone has the right to take part in the government of his country, directly or through freely chosen representatives. ◆

UNITED NATIONS

84

It Isn't Right...

One of the aims of a school assembly must be to foster idealism and encourage students to become active citizens rather than helpless cogs in the machine of society. There will be times when they wish to protest (fairly and not merely disruptively) over parochial, regional or national issues. In such circumstances, they may well feel powerless.

This article was written for Christian Aid News *to help Christian Aid supporters pursue their aims by involving their MPs. This article may be usefully read whenever students feel strongly about an issue.*

So you feel it isn't right that . . . ? And you feel nothing can be done? There is something you can do. You can write to your MP.

◆

MPs OFTEN SAY the strength of public opinion on an issue shows up best in the size of their mailbag.

Writing a letter to your MP is one of the most practical and simple initiatives you can take. Apart from voting, it is the most basic form of political action that our democracy encourages! For the average busy and committed person it also takes very little time. Yet it can be an effective ways of showing concern and involving others, especially those who may be in a position to influence government policy.

Here are a few ideas to help you. They may not all apply to your situation, but they are easily adaptable and will help you to have ideas of your own. ☛

- Keep your letter short and confine it to one issue.

- Refer to recent information which makes it topical.

- Write in your own words.

- Give personal reasons for your concern. Add a note of urgency but not of outrage. Try to convince your MP.

- Don't assume any previous knowledge on the part of the MP – you may well be the expert! MPs are often grateful to hear from their constituents on a new issue and like to be more informed.

- Ask questions that require a factual answer, e.g. 'Is it true that . . . ?' Ask your MP to pass on your views to a minister for comment. Allow two or three weeks for a reply. Follow up your letter and, if you are not satisfied with the reply, write again.

- Don't feel that statistics are always necessary; they help, but arguments are more important.

- Send a copy of your letter to one or two other prominent people in your area, or obtain other signatories, e.g. clergy or councillors. It often encourages your MP to know that others are involved – the 'halo effect'.

- Publicise the issue if you can, by writing a similar letter to your local newspaper. Refer to something topical or think of a local angle.

- Above all, don't give up because you think your concern is just a 'drop in the ocean'. Remember how many more people in the world the issue concerns, whose voices are not being heard, even though our government's policies may affect them. ◆

JOHN MONTAGU

85

Crime and Punishment

The aim of this assembly is to help pupils to become aware of the antisocial nature of some offences, to develop an awareness of the consequences of such wrongdoing, and to consider what constitutes a fair punishment. One way of using the passage would be simply to read out the eight offences and to ask students to put them in order of increasing seriousness. Another activity would be to take the offences one by one, perhaps over a series of assemblies, and to discuss suitable punishments. (Individuals or groups could each write down an apt punishment for one offence, and then larger groups could decide the most effective or fairest punishment of those offered.)

Possible punishments that they may or may not think of could include:

- *Conditional discharge (the offender has to behave well for a certain period of time; if there is any sort of bad behaviour, then the offender can be sentenced again for the first crime as well as for the new one).*
- *Fines.*
- *Attendance at an attendance centre.*
- *A period of discipline and hard work at a detention centre.*
- *Committal to a young offenders' institution.*

Joy-riding in cars

Two fifteen-year-olds take a car and drive it away. They are obviously uninsured. They leave it abandoned yet undamaged on some waste ground. The owner was desperately worried while it was missing and was put to a great deal of inconvenience. It is their second offence. ☞

Shoplifting

A sixteen-year-old girl steals a wrist-watch which she plans to sell. She intends to give the money to her boyfriend, who is a drug addict. It is her first offence.

Vandalism

Four sixteen-year-old boys are caught in the act of wrecking a telephone-box. They are drunk. It is their first offence.

Mugging

A fifteen-year-old girl attacks an old lady with a knife. She runs off with the old lady's handbag straight into the arms of a police officer who has heard the lady's screams. The lady loses the sight of one eye and, on discharge from hospital, is too scared to move from her home. It is the girl's third offence. The previous offences were shoplifting and assault.

Under-age drinking

Three boys and three girls, all aged thirteen, are found drinking cider in a shed. They are all making a lot of noise. It is their first offence.

Housebreaking

A fourteen-year-old boy is caught in the act of housebreaking. He has just sprayed paint all over the walls. He has already been in trouble for joy-riding in cars.

Unlawful sexual intercourse

After pressure from her parents, a fifteen-year-old girl has admitted having sexual intercourse with her boyfriend of the ☞

same age. She has been 'on the pill' for some time. They had been planning to run away together when they reached sixteen.

Fighting

The police are summoned to a youth club. Two fourteen-year-old boys are fighting and when the police enter they see that each is bleeding and each has a broken bottle in his hand. Both are equally at fault. It is their first offence. ◆

VALUES

86

Obituary for a Housewife

Before reading this passage, pupils may need an explanation of what a newspaper 'obituary' is, and may need to be shown examples from some of the broadsheet daily papers. Beyond that, this passage should need no further introduction.

SOME FEMINISTS SHOUT for equal pay for equal work, others want abortion on demand. All I am asking is that women be treated like men on the obituary page.

When a man fades away, he gets a write-up about all the things he has achieved and all the places he has been. When a housewife dies, if she gets even a line or two, the obituary is still about all the things her *husband* has achieved and all the places *he* has been.

As a suggestion I would like to present the following obituary for a housewife that is patterned after the hundreds of eulogies I have read for prominent men. This is an obituary for a prominent *housewife:*

Mrs Ima Martar died following a brief illness of botulism poisoning contracted after eating some of her own home canning.

Those who knew her will recall that during the past twenty-five years, Mrs Martar cooked three meals a day, plus snacks. Her laundry was always sunshine bright, and she will be remembered as an innovator since she was the first on her street to add a fabric softener to her wash. Never in her entire life did she scorch a garment while she ironed. No one excelled her when it came to mopping floors.

Before her death, Mrs Martar was a national holder of the award that goes to the woman who for seven years never missed a single episode of *As the World Turns*. Mrs Martar often remarked how thrilled she was at the time she was approached to do a free testimonial for a detergent company.

Mrs Martar's most admirable qualities were that she took a leading vitamin regularly so that her husband 'would keep her', and she chose the brand of coffee that would repel her nosy neighbour, Mrs Olsen. Thanks to hair colouring, there was not a single grey hair in Mrs Martar's head, and one of the most welcome breaks in her day was when the travelling cosmetic woman came around.

Mrs Martar is survived by two sons, both of whom are grown with wives of their own. They will barely notice that she is no longer here except when vacation time rolls around and they realise there is no free place to leave the kids.

She will be sorely missed by her husband until a respectable time has passed so that he can marry one of his former secretaries whom he has been supporting for years.

Mrs Martar's final words, whispered into the ears of a nearby nurse, were that in lieu of flowers would her friends, *please,* send donations to a local, state, or national Women's Liberation group. ◆

MILDRED KAVANAUGH

87

Well, Well, Well

This short story has a delightful sting in its tail and is best read by two female voices of roughly the same age – to keep us guessing. With some rehearsal it can have considerable dramatic impact. It is also a way into discussion of the issue of the right to life of a baby versus a mother's rights.

You probably know there are many arguments about the question of abortion. Should a mother in all cases have the baby she has conceived or are there times when it is right to have an abortion? Before we discuss any of the issues, here is a conversation between a mother and her teenage daughter.

◆

'WELL YOU OBVIOUSLY can't keep it.'

'What do you mean, *can't* keep it? Who says I can't?'

'It's obvious – you'll have to have an abortion.'

'I don't want an abortion, I want to . . . '

'You can't, just think about it for a minute.'

'I have thought about it, I've thought about it a lot.'

'But you've just started college.'

'I know I've just started college, but there's a crèche there.'

'Oh, I see, you're going to go in pregnant and have the baby in between lectures.'

'It's due in the holidays and anyway I can get time off, other people have done it before, you know.'

'That's doesn't mean you have to, though, does it. And what about money?'

'I'll manage.'

'What, on a grant, with a baby and no father.'

'Yes on a grant, with a baby and no father – that's what's really worrying you, isn't it? Bloody hell, in this day and age!'

'Well, it would help if you would say who the father is, or don't you know?'

'Of course I know, but I don't want him to.'

'Why not, for heaven's sake, he ought to pay for it – you could get maintenance you know or he could pay for an abortion.'

'I don't want him to pay for anything and I am *not* having an abortion.'

'He's not married, is he?'

'No, he's not married.'

'Then I don't see . . . '

'I just don't want anyone interfering, that's all.'

'Well, you needn't worry on my account – I'm not having anything to do with it and don't expect me to baby-sit either.'

'No one asked you to.'

'Not yet, but you just wait. Honestly, I thought *you* were old enough to know better. It's embarrassing.'

'You'll be saying 'What will the neighbours say?' next.'

'I don't give a damn about the neighbours, but they will think things if there's no father.'

'There is a father!'

'Oh yes, an anonymous one.'

'I *know* who he is.'

☛

253

'Well, at least tell me.'

'No. Look, I made a decision, I got pregnant on purpose. I want to have this baby, OK?'

'But *Mum* – at your age!' ◆

KATE HALL

88

Plagues and Pandemics

The AIDS epidemic has many things in common with other plagues that have attacked the human race over the centuries. That is not, to suggest that it is the 'plague' of anyone in particular. It involves us all, just as did the Black Death and other pandemics.

Obviously this is a controversial issue, but one that cannot be ignored. This passage is offered as a complement to the sort of health education that will be available from other sources and is an attempt to put AIDS into an historical context, as well as airing two common reactions: denial of its importance, and desires for hasty, unfair 'retribution'. This is a longish passage and may be used over two separate assemblies.

You probably all know something about AIDS. It has some-times been called the 'Twentieth Century Plague'. It *is* in fact a fairly new illness and one that we still know little about. But similar illnesses have swept the world in previous centuries and caused similar panics.

◆

THE BLACK DEATH is perhaps the best-known world epidemic. It began in 1346 and spread through India, Tartary, Mesopotamia, Syria and Armenia. By 1347 it had reached Hungary, Italy and Spain; a year later France and Germany. It finally arrived in England in 1349. It had run its course in three years, but by then it had killed one-third of Europe's inhabitants. The Black Death was followed by sporadic outbreaks of bubonic plague throughout the next three centuries, one of these being the Great Plague of 1665 in London.

Epidemics of meningitis occurred in France and Germany in 1482. There were outbreaks of the 'Sweating Sickness', causing considerable mortality, in 1485, 1499, 1506, 1517 and 1551. ☞

Syphilis first appeared in Europe in an epidemic form at the end of the fifteenth century. The most learned physicians of that period described it as a new disease which they had never seen before. The disease spread rapidly through Italy, and appeared in France, Germany and Switzerland in 1495. It had reached Holland and Greece by 1496, and a year later England and Scotland. It finally arrived in Hungary and Russia in 1499.

The syphilis plague is an important one to look at as in some respects it prefigures the AIDS epidemic. It was a new disease, spread mainly through sexual means. It was also thought to be spread by the public bath-houses, and after syphilis appeared many of these were closed. It spread widely in some countries for more than four years before other countries saw any cases at all. The terrible tragedy of congenital infection was found to occur, a mother infected with syphilis passing it to her baby in the womb. People became so conscious of syphilis that many other conditions were confused with it and wrongly attributed to it. People who were infected with syphilis and infectious to others passed it on while they still seemed healthy, before the severe crusting, disfiguring sores appeared which identified them as syphilitic.

Syphilis was untreatable; there was then no cure. Ultimately it was usually fatal, sometimes after years of illness. It spread widely in the population of Europe.

The most recent pandemic, this time of influenza, broke out in 1918 in a world already decimated by war. In twelve weeks 1 billion people, half the world's population at the time, were affected by virulent influenza. Twenty-two million died.

Cholera epidemics have now become past history in Europe, while smallpox, once the scourge of whole areas, has now been eradicated. In the nineteenth century 400,000 Europeans were ☞

dying from smallpox every year, and by the mid-twentieth century between 10 and 15 million people in thirty-three countries were infected, with 2 million people dying from it every year. After a campaign lasting ten years, the World Health Organization finally tracked down the last case of smallpox and eradicated the disease in 1975.

What common factors can we see in people's reactions to these fearful epidemics?

Denial and fear

People's first response to an impending disaster of great magnitude is often to deny it. This has been so with epidemic diseases in the past and many would maintain that the common reaction during the early years of the AIDS epidemic has been one of denial. The reasons for this are threefold:

- The human brain does not want to accept that something terrible is happening.
- The authorities want to prevent panic, and so they may at first refuse to acknowledge the situation publicly.
- To admit that a disaster is coming means taking action to avert it. If for any reason that action cannot be decided upon or cannot be implemented, then denial is the easiest official course.

The desire for action

When once the temptation to deny a danger is overcome, there follows a desire to do something to avert it. This action may sometimes be quite inappropriate. During the bubonic plagues of the Middle Ages, groups of people were made scapegoats. People also thought it would help to carry sweetsmelling pomanders.

But sometimes the action is appropriate to the danger.

Public health measures against plague were first developed in Europe during the fourteenth century. Plague arrived in Venice in January 1348, and two months later the Venetians appointed a special cabinet committee of three noblemen to consider what measures should be taken. These special measures included:

- New burial places away from the city.
- A special service of barges to carry the dead.
- The dead to be buried at least five feet underground.
- The release of all debtors from gaol.
- Strict control of immigration and shipping.
- Quarantine stations, where the sick and those surviving the disease were isolated for forty days. Quarantine also included travellers and goods from infected areas.

In 1399 there was fumigation during plague, houses were ventilated and the bedding of those who had died from plague was burned. People were not allowed to live in plague houses for a period of time following the death of the victims.

Today, in facing the AIDS pandemic which may prove even more serious than almost any previous plague, we need to learn from history.

The first lesson is not to deny the reality of the danger. When people are properly informed, they will begin to co-operate in preventive measures.

The next is that such measures need to cover whole societies. Epidemics are no respecters of boundaries.

But yet each plague is unique, AIDS not least of all. In some ways it is like no illness we have seen before. There is no way to ☞

protect ourselves from it apart from avoiding infection. Its only limiting factor lies in the number of people exposed to it. And there is no known cure. ◆

DR CAROLINE COLLIER

89

Accidents Will Happen

Some disasters or tragedies seem to be 'natural' and inevitable. Others are clearly man-made. One of the commonest tragedies to afflict teenagers is the road traffic accident. This passage consists of excerpts from a book by Andrew Tricker, which describes what happened when his 50cc bike crashed into the back of a lorry. As a result of this accident he became paralysed. It is offered as an encouragement to safe driving. It is also a passage that shows how, in adversity, we often learn what matters most to us.

This reading was written by Andrew Tricker when he was a young man and an apprentice mechanic working for his City and Guilds exams. The story begins one cold Friday afternoon when he is riding home from college on his 50cc bike with some friends who are also on their bikes. It begins to rain and then, as they approach a hill, the rain becomes much heavier.

◆

AS WE WENT down into the small dip we got some relief from the rain from a large bank on the right, but as we started up the small incline the rain met us head-on again and I had to lower my head once more. We were just coming to the end of the new piece of road when I thought it was time to look up again.

It was then that I got the impression that there was a shadow in front of me. I looked up – I only had a split second to act and in one flowing movement I wound down the throttle, jammed on my brakes and pushed back with all my might. At the same moment I heard this high pitched noise in my ears and felt as if I had done a complete somersault. It must have been only a ☞

matter of seconds before I came to, and as I opened my eyes I could see something above me. I realised that I was underneath the back end of a lorry. I thought, 'Crumbs, I'd better get up just in case he decides to drive away.' I motioned my body to sit up but nothing happened. I realised from a previous accident that I could be suffering from shock so decided to relax for a moment. It was then that I started to hear voices, one I recognised as my friend Kim's, the other one said, 'Are you OK?'

Andy discovers that he can't move, nor can he feel his legs. He is eventually taken to hospital by ambulance. He has a period when he remembers very little of what has happened. In fact, he has broken his neck and may never walk again. But he is eventually taken to Stoke Mandeville Hospital where another doctor speaks to his parents.

'Mrs and Mrs Tricker, I wonder, would you step into my office for a few moments.'

They got up from their chairs and walked into his office; a sliding door was pulled across to prevent me from hearing their conversation, but months later Mum told me what he had said.

'Sit down, please Mr and Mrs Tricker. Andrew has had a very serious accident and has damaged the sixth vertebra in his neck and has also damaged his spinal cord – to what extent at the moment we cannot say. I must tell you that your son could die at any time in the next two weeks. Now, you can stay at a hostel just over the road if you want, or have you got other people to think about back home?' The news that I could die had not crossed their minds until that moment and was another terrible shock to them.

Andrew Tricker was lucky. He did not die. By the time he wrote the book he had started to walk in a walking brace and ☛

could manage a few steps. He hoped to make further progress. This is what he wrote towards the end of his book.

In the years that have passed since my accident I have learnt a great deal about myself and other people. For instance, before my accident I thought that money was everything. I remember thinking when I was at work how hard done by I was not having enough money to buy a car, or even to last me over the week once I had been out for a drink at the weekend. If a little windfall should come my way, I thought, what a great difference it would make to my life. Here I am now, with nearly three thousand pounds in the bank, that I have been able to save over the last five years, but I am far worse off now than I have ever been. It's strange as I sit here and listen to other people moaning about how hard up they are, if only they realised how much richer they were than an awful lot of people in this world. It amazes me how much preference people give to material things like owning their houses, having the best furniture and buying a new car just to stand it out in front of their homes so that everyone can see it. Although it is nice to have these things, and for those who haven't got any more than a roof over their heads they are good things to dream about, to me they are nice but not essential. To me someone who is well off or rich is the person who has his health and has also got lots of friends and people who like or love him. I look at it like this: a new car or a three-piece suite can't listen to you when you're low or show you any affection and they cannot come and visit you when you're ill in hospital or lying on your death bed. Lots of people lead a very lonely existence because they have considered possessions to be more important than friends. ◆

ANDY TRICKER

90

On the Streets

*The two passages that follow are taken from a report published by
Centrepoint Soho on the first twenty years of its work with homeless
young people. The passages may encourage young people to think how
they can help those less fortunate than themselves and may also usefully
discourage any ideas of leaving home without a destination.*

*The first passage requires three readers: two to read the parts of
Darren and James (young homeless teenagers) and one to read that of
the official at the Department of Social Security. The second passage,
'On The Streets', is about the realities of homelessness in Soho. Dean
Street is one of the thoroughfares in that area.*

There may be moments when you feel fed up and frustrated
with the place you live and with your present way of life.
How tempting, you might think, to get away from it all: to
find a new life amid the glamour of London's West End. Many
young people have this idea every year, and run away to
London where they find themselves reduced to homelessness
and to begging. If you leave home without work to go to or a
place to study, you may have great difficulty in finding help.

◆

One Aspect of Homelessness

Darren and James spend a frustrating morning answering
questions at the DSS.

OFFICIAL: Have you any money?
DARREN: No.
OFFICIAL: Have you any savings in excess of £500?
JAMES: What?
OFFICIAL: Are you pregnant?

DARREN: No.

OFFICIAL: Are you blind?

JAMES: No.

OFFICIAL: Are you married?

DARREN: No.

OFFICIAL: How old are your children?

JAMES: [*looks astonished*]

OFFICIAL: Are your children employed?

DARREN: I'm eighteen!

OFFICIAL: Do your children contribute to the Community Charge/council tax?

JAMES: I'm *eighteen.*

OFFICIAL: Are you disabled?

DARREN: No.

OFFICIAL: Have you worked in the past six months?

JAMES: No.

OFFICIAL: Do you expect any back pay from your last employer?

DARREN: [*looks very puzzled*]

OFFICIAL: Have you ever claimed before?

JAMES: No.

OFFICIAL: When was the last time you claimed?

DARREN: Never.

OFFICIAL: Do you live with your parents?

JAMES: No.

OFFICIAL: Why did you leave home?

DARREN: Violence.

OFFICIAL: Is it possible to go home?

JAMES: [*looks incredulous*]

OFFICIAL: Have you been living in this country for the past six years?

DARREN: Every ✳✳✳✳✳✳ day.

OFFICIAL: Where did you sleep last night?

☛

JAMES: Streets.

OFFICIAL: Do you own any land or property?

DARREN: No, I don't think so.

OFFICIAL: Are you working at present?

JAMES: No, I don't think so.

OFFICIAL: Have you any lodgers or tenants?

DARREN: No, I'm pretty sure.

On the Streets

This is a poem written by a young homeless person living in the Soho area of London. Dean Street is one of the main streets in that part of the city:

How many times can you cross Dean Street in the course of a day?
The streets of Soho sound and smell of action, glamour, success, excitement. The cabs, the bikers, the lorries they never let you through.
You're walking about, at eighteen, in the ashes of a lifetime and you can't cross the street,
And they don't care. They pass you by.

You and your mates, living in a box.
Living in a cardboard box.
Living in cardboard boxes can't really be a good idea otherwise more people would do it.
'No problem, you'd prefer a cardboard box to a three-bedroomed semi, we can arrange that, Sir.'
Estate agents don't often say that, do they?
And people walk past you and think, 'Homelessness, it's bad, but it's there' instead of thinking 'It's there and it's bad'.

You still can't get across Dean Street. The traffic, the movement.

☛

If you die sleeping on the streets, you die of natural causes. How can the way you live be thought to be unnatural but your death natural?

Tony has spent several years on the streets. He has noticed the difference.
'Different now. Different. All kids now.
Children. Children sleeping on the streets. When I was a nipper we'd heard about the stuff happening in Victorian times. Not now. Couldn't believe it.
Begging. Nippers begging.'

Begging. You know how to do it. 'Homeless, Hungry, Help Me' cards everywhere.
But that doesn't hide the pain, the suffering, the awfulness of sleeping on the streets.
The dreadful feeling of not being as good as the people walking by.
The terrifying fear of another, yet another, night hiding in a corner hoping you won't be noticed, hoping you don't matter but praying you do.

And you still have to cross Dean Street with nowhere to go when you get there. ◆

CENTREPOINT SOHO

91

Police – Friend or Foe?

In many schools 'the police' is not an issue. In some, a police liaison visit is an easy-going occasion, and the friendly neighbourhood bobby a welcome visitor. In others, the presence of the police would provoke considerable tension. This passage simply outlines the debate about the police and helps to show how the issue is not as simple as it appears to some people. It might also serve to introduce a debate or discussion.

We expect the police to protect property, to catch criminals, control traffic and clear up accidents. Even so, to some (or even many) people, the police are the enemy. Yet would even these people say that we could manage without a police force? How do you see the police – friend or foe?

♦

ONE OF THE main problems facing a democratic society is how to use its police force to protect citizens from crime and disorder without taking away their right to behave as they wish. Some argue that without the police there would be no freedom at all. Others say the police are more concerned with control than they are with liberty.

But the police have an enormous range of other duties outside crime and public order. These, too, affect the way that people see them.

Your friendly policeman?

Inevitably, people's reaction to the police has much to do with their own personal experience. Research shows that those living in well-kept suburbs or richer neighbourhoods trust and ☞

like the police more than those living in poorer areas, especially the inner cities.

The British *Police Instruction Book*, issued in the nineteenth century, stated that 'the primary object of an efficient police force is the prevention of crime; the next that of detection and punishment of offenders if crime is committed'. Recruits still memorise these words.

In fact, the police forces in most countries now also control crowds and traffic, protect politicians, diplomats and important foreign visitors, deal with lost property, break the news of death to families and help in every kind of emergency. One-third of all calls to the police in America are for help where no crime is involved.

Most members of the police come from families who are not well-off, but sociologists have shown that they acquire middle-class attitudes to property and obedience during their working lives. There is no evidence that those who join the police have specially authoritarian personalities at the point of joining. But some recruits at least may be attracted by fast cars and the hope of an exciting working life.

A justified fear?

To many people the sight of a police uniform causes fear and an uneasy feeling of guilt, whether deserved or not. In practice, most meetings between police and public are to do with motoring, and this has undoubtedly had a bad effect on the public's view of the police.

Another pressure point is the relationship between police and young people. Police are accused of being automatically suspicious of young people, particularly if they belong to ethnic minorities. They are also accused of indiscriminate ☞

searches of youngsters, using this as a way of disciplining and controlling young people rather than directly trying to deal with crime.

Even more serious is the charge that the police may themselves be prepared to bend the law in order to keep down crime and anti-social behaviour. Studies in America have shown that police see themselves as law and order 'craftsmen', entitled to do what they think fit to maintain public order, and often unwilling to accept the restrictions placed on them by the courts.

Police in many countries have been found guilty of planting evidence and extracting confessions under duress. This may indicate an enthusiasm to control people whom they consider wrongdoers. But when it happens, it greatly undermines public confidence in the police. ◆

ADAM HOPKINS AND GABY MACPHEDRAN

92

Sobura's Story

This passage is taken from Common Cause, *the magazine of the charity called ActionAid. It tells the story of a Bangladeshi woman who, despite her sufferings, had managed to cling fiercely to what she considers her most important possession: her self-respect. The passage usefully counters any feeling that the Third World is populated entirely by people waiting to have aid handed to them.*

This is the story of Sobura Katum. She lives on an island in the delta of the River Ganges in Bangladesh. It is an area that suffers from cyclones, storms and flooding. She is fifty-five, and has had more than enough trouble to last a lifetime – but has never given up. As you listen to her story, you might think what is the most important thing that she has in her life. Her story begins with her own words.

◆

'I HAVE HAD many sorrows in my life. It was in my destiny. I have been widowed three times. I have borne eleven children, of whom only three are still living. Yet for me the worst days are over. I have my strength and I'm independent again. I look after my family myself. I depend upon the charity of no one.'

Her story begins in northern Bhola, an island in the Ganga delta of Bangladesh. Her grandfather was skilled in herbal medicine and one of Sobura's earliest memories is of being cured by one of his remedies. Encouraged by her father, she began to study and absorb her grandfather's medical knowledge.

She was virtually a child herself when first she married and soon was the mother of three. When the eldest became seriously ill ☛

with diarrhoea, she cured him with one of her herbal medicines.

Impressed, her neighbours began asking for her help and soon she had earned a reputation as a skilful maker of medicines. But her talents were no match for the endemic diseases of Bhola. Within a few years, she lost her husband to dysentery and malnutrition carried off her three children.

Sobura married again and bore two more sons, a remarkable sign of good fortune in the Moslem society of Bangladesh. But further tragedy was to strike. One child died from malnutrition and her second husband fell a victim to dysentery. So she married a third time, a farmer from Bhola, and she gave him two more sons.

'In 1970, Bangladesh suffered a terrible cyclone and Bhola was right in its path. It had been drizzling all morning and then, at about noon, the wind suddenly started to gust strongly. By evening time, the whole house was shaking. I stood in the doorway so that if it collapsed, we would all be safe.

'Before long, the howling wind began to drive the sea inland. I grabbed the smallest child – my husband was away working – and spent the night moving from tree to tree, clinging to anything solid and trying to keep one step ahead of the flood waters. I remember saying my prayers so many times that my jaw ached with the effort.

'By morning, I had managed to reach some relatives and they took us in. The floods had started to recede so I waded back to see what was left of our home. I found my husband, but not our three young sons who had been working for a farmer on an islet some distance away. It lay in the path of the huge tidal wave that swept in from the sea. We never saw them again.

For days there was no food, no fuel and nothing to drink. ☛

although we were surrounded by water. Death infected the river and filled the air with its smell. After a few days, I was given some relief flour, but when I got home, I accidentally dropped the earthenware pot in which I had collected it. The flour fell on to the floor which was swimming in filthy water. I just stood there looking at it. After all we had been through, it was somehow just too much to bear. It was the one moment when I nearly gave up. I cried out to God to help me.'

The cyclone destroyed most of Sobura's possessions and the floods washed away all of the family land, sweeping it downstream in a brown cloud of silt. Their only choice was to trek south to the squatter lands of Char Fassion where they lived in a house her husband built. For many years, Sobura supported the family and her ailing husband by cleaning rice in the homes of the rich or selling homemade medicines.

In 1981, he died and she borrowed 400 *taka* (£8) to pay for the funeral. Unable to repay the loan, she ended by selling the house, leaving the family homeless and destitute.

'The next five years were the worst of my life. I had absolutely nothing and was reduced to begging. It filled me with shame. My father had been an honourable man and to be dependent upon the charity of others caused me great pain. For a while I joined a Food for Work scheme, but it was very tough and I was weak from lack of food. I hurt myself and had to give it up. Eventually I found the *kendro.*'

Two years ago, Sobura joined an ActionAid credit scheme on Bhola Island and took out an 800 taka loan (£16), sufficient to help her to break out of the grim spiral into which her life had fallen.

'At last, I could throw off the shame of begging and use my own skills to help us. I started up my herbal medicine business again ☞

and I bought rushes to weave the mats which my sons sell in the market after school. I kept up the repayments on the first loan and took out a second one to buy a cow. It grazes on a farmer's land and he will take the first calf but we keep the milk. I breed ducks and chickens for sale. I also act as midwife to local women. They pay me in soap, hair oil or, if I'm lucky, a sari. They accept me as a sister. They can tell me their troubles and they know I'll do my best to help.

'Life is hard and I never have a moment's rest. We could be turned off this land at any time but I have my strength and, if I have to move on, I'll cope. At least I know that I am no longer dependent upon anyone. It is my own hard work, my knowledge and my skill which keeps the family going. I have my pride back.' ◆

OLIVIA BENNETT

93

Leprosy

Leprosy remains one of the most serious and troublesome diseases in the world. Those who suffer from leprosy (the word 'leper' is best avoided) are often regarded as 'different' from those who suffer from any other disease. Although people of all races and social levels can catch the disease, over 90 per cent of cases occur in the Third World. This mini-anthology of passages about leprosy may help pupils to understand something about an illness that some people regard as 'merely' biblical, and others believe (wrongly) to be incurable.

(Note: World Leprosy Day is the last Sunday in January. The story of how Jesus healed a man suffering from leprosy can be found in Matthew 8.1–4 or in Mark 1.40–45.)

There are several stories in the Bible about people who suffer from leprosy. Today there are still 15 million people in the world who have the disease. Five million of these are children under the age of fifteen. People who suffer from leprosy are often looked upon with fear and loathing. In some lands they are still not allowed to own property or to attend school – or even be admitted to a hospital. So what is leprosy? You may think of it as a disease, which, if you catch it, may result in your fingers or toes dropping off. But what is it really?

Caused by a bacillus (a kind of bacteria), leprosy is a mildly infectious disease otherwise known as 'Hansen's Disease'.

It affects mainly the nerves, skin, eyes and nose and is not hereditary. If untreated, the extremities may become numb. It is this loss of feeling that can lead to deformity.

Leprosy can be completely cured today for as little as £6–£18, using multidrug therapy (MDT). Early treatment can prevent permanent damage or deformity from occurring.

But many people can still be very cruel to those who suffer ☞

from the disease – as this story about a woman called Miti
shows:

———————————— ◆ ————————————

THE THREE BOYS ran away as the last stone hit the ground.
A crumpled heap twitched for a moment, then slumped silently.
The monsoon hadn't arrived yet and dust flew up from the
passing vehicle over the bundle below.

'Stop!' Francine started, shouting above the noise of the worn
engine. 'Amon, what's that?' Together, she and the paramedic
pulled up to identify the stranger. Prominent bones peeped
through dirty rags, and pulling back the hood Francine made
out a little, wizened face.

It was Miti. Francine recognised her from a few years back,
when she had gone for treatment on a foot ulcer. Carrying her
gently to the jeep, they made full speed ahead for Medan . . .

The hospital was alive with the bustle, noise and chatter of an
out-patient's clinic. This morning was special because many
patients had finished their multidrug therapy courses and were
being released from treatment, fully cured.

Francine made her way to the women's ward and found Miti
sitting on her bed.

'Good morning, Miti. How are you today?' She needn't have
asked. Miti was in a sorry state, her hands badly swollen, feet
badly deformed – far more than before – with a foul-smelling
ulcer on her left one. Her face was puffy and swollen, the left eye
inflamed, and she was very malnourished.

Yet, by the grace of God she was alive. To Francine, any life was
precious, worth fighting for.

Gradually Miti confided in her new friend about the events that
had changed her life so drastically.

In a nutshell: she had lost everything. Her husband had thrown her out on discovering she had leprosy. Following her one morning to the clinic – thinking she was having a 'liaison' with some local fellow, he discovered her secret, and threw her out in fear.

She took her four-year-old son, Vitu, with her. In Indonesia children bring status to a woman. Now Vitu was all she had left.

They survived at first; Miti finding work in a village many miles away – weaving and doing domestic chores. But living so far from the leprosy clinic, she missed her treatment and the visible signs began to show. With clawed hands and a loping gait, no one wanted to know . . . She met with rejection time and again.

So, she began to beg, turning her disability to her advantage. At first this was profitable, but with increasing neglect her deformities worsened, and passers-by didn't want to come anywhere near. In these remote areas there was still a great deal of health education to be done . . .

Then tragedy struck. Little Vitu caught an infection, complicated with malnutrition and pneumonia, and died.

Miti had lost everything and just wanted to die. She tried to beg, but with no heart in it. Children jeered and threw stones. Folk passed by as if she blended with the dirt beneath their feet.

Now though, she was in a safe haven – for a time. At Medan hospital she would receive loving care, warmth and food. She could never be fully independent again, but they would see her settled somewhere nearby. Surgery would help correct some of the damage to her limbs and before long the face that looked seventy-five would resume its correct mid-thirties appearance . . .

The real tragedy, though, was that the difficulties need never ☞

have arisen in the first place. With the right medical care disability could have been prevented. With health education those boys need never have thrown stones at Miti, or her husband thrown her out. With plenty of loving care there need never be the isolation and hurt when outward beauty is marred and inner beauty trampled over . . .

Yet, by the grace of God, they had survived and were moving on to brighter horizons.

By the grace of God, thought Francine . . . by the grace of God.

The Counting Game

(A prayer of a child with leprosy)

Have you lots of fingers?
Play at counting . . . One to Ten
Have you lots of toes so you can play the game again . . .
Is your skin unbroken
Smooth in every dip and rise –
When you meet with strangers
Do they smile into your eyes?
Can you, do you, do they?
Tell me, is it really true?
Will you come and count my fingers so that I can be like
    you . . .
Will you gently hold my body
Knowing every dip and rise
But most of all – no stranger,
Would you love me with your eyes? ◆

GRAHAM AYLMER

94

What's Your Poison?

This reading and the next focus attention on the importance of water, especially in the developing world. Much endemic illness could be avoided were it only possible to provide supplies of clean water. The information in this passage is taken from a VSO leaflet.

In Britain, we use water as if there were no tomorrow – even in those summers when there is a lack of rain. A family uses an average of 22 to 60 gallons a day! It may take a couple of gallons to wash a few cups. Three gallons to flush the lavatory. When we wash a child's hands under a running tap, it takes a gallon and a half. A car wash takes a minimum of 25 gallons. An automatic household washing-machine can use over 60 gallons for an average load of washing. But in the Third World there are millions of people who cannot gain access to even one cup of clean water.

◆

IN THE DEVELOPING world five million children under the age of five will die this year from diseases caused and spread by dirty water. Adults will suffer too. Many killer diseases, such as cholera, typhoid and malaria, thrive in the insanitary conditions that prevail when clean, safe water is not available.

Here are some of the 'poisons' that Third World children and families will be drinking today because they lack the most basic of all necessities of life – clean, safe water:

Soap and laundry dirt

Clothes are washed in local streams and ponds – often the only source of water available. The same water is then used for cooking and domestic use.

Eye diseases

The flies that spread eye diseases breed and live wherever dirty water exists. Repeated infection is a major cause of blindness in the Third World.

Village rubbish

In the rainy season, all types of rubbish and filth will be washed into the local water supply: rotting vegetation, discarded food, and the flies and bacteria that feed off them.

Typhoid, cholera, hepatitis

Outbreaks of killer diseases occur when water supplies become contaminated. Hepatitis, cholera, typhoid and other diseases thrive in insanitary conditions.

Diarrhoeal disease

The bacteria that carry the many different kinds of diarrhoeal disease also thrive in filthy water. Babies and young children under five are especially vulnerable.

Animal and human waste

At night wild animals will often use the communal village water supply. In the day domesticated animals – cattle, sheep and goats – take their turn. Humans, too, bathe and carry out their toilet in the local stream.

Despite all these dangers, in many, many places safe water could easily be provided. Often a simple well just a few metres deep is all that is required. Together with pit latrines, these will go a long way towards reducing the ranges of disease, and greatly improving the daily lives of thousands of people whose lives are already very hard. ◆

VOLUNTARY SERVICE OVERSEAS

95

Water of Life

In this second reading about water, we consider its religious significance. (This passage is possibly more suited to older students. Links may be made here with the RE syllabus.)

You know that many people in the world are desperately short of clean water. Clean water is vital for a healthy life. Much has been done, but much remains to be done, to help people in the developing world to receive supplies of adequate drinking water. But water is important for other reasons as well . . .

❖

A GREAT DEAL has been done in recent years to improve water supplies in the Third World, but drought in Africa and the fact that three out of five people alive today in developing countries still have no easy access to safe drinking water should remind us just how vital water is to human life.

Perhaps it is our dependence on water that gives it such an important role in the world's religions. Indeed, in the story of the creation (as told in the Bible book of Genesis), the world itself is made out of 'the waters of the deep': 'And the Spirit of God moved upon the face of the waters . . . And God said, Let there be a firmament in the midst of the waters . . . '

A similar idea is found in Hindu scriptures where, in the sacred text known as the Upanishads, we can read: 'In the beginning this world was water. Water produced the Truth and the truth is Brahman [*the World Spirit*].'

Water has, however, a continuing significance in Hinduism – in particular in the form of the holy River Ganges. For Hindus, all ☞

rivers are to some extent holy, not least because they are so necessary to the process of growing crops and sustaining life. But the Ganges is considered to be especially holy. To Hindus it is 'Ganga Ma' or 'Mother Ganges' and every Hindu hopes one day to bathe in its waters and so to have his or her sins washed away. To drink its water, having bathed in it, and to carry away bottles of its water for those who have not had the good fortune to bathe in it themselves, is thought to be an especially good and generous act.

Some Hindus make the long and difficult pilgrimage high up into the Himalayas to the source of the Ganges and there they cheerfully bathe in its icy waters! Many Hindus hope to die near the river and (after cremation) to have their ashes scattered on the river. These will then be carried away to be joined with 'the world spirit'.

The idea of water as something that cleanses and purifies occurs in many religions. For example, in Judaism a *mikveh* is a pool or 'gathering' of rain water collected in a specially designed container. It is used at special times for bathing and for other purposes.

Water as a means of purification is also important to Muslims. Five times a day a Muslim must answer the 'call to prayer' but, before these prayers, he or she must make him- or herself clean. This procedure is called *wudu*. It not only removes any dirt so that the person is not defiled in any way while addressing God, but it also helps to concentrate the mind. *Wudu* begins with the Muslim washing his or her hands, then the mouth and nose followed by the whole of the face. After this, the right hand and lower arm and then the left hand and lower arm are washed; the head is wiped and finally the ears and feet are washed.

Water also has its place in Christianity. Natural springs of water ☞

are often associated with healing and pilgrims travel to drink or bathe in these springs to be cured of an illness. Especially famous springs are at Lourdes in southern France and at the Shrine of Our Lady (the mother of Jesus) at Walsingham in Norfolk.

Christians (and Sikhs) use water in baptism services whereby people become a member of these religions. In Sikh baptism, the baby is fed a little *amrit* (a mixture of water and sugar). The water is a sign of life and strength, the sugar a sign of gentleness and kindness.

In some Christian churches, baptism takes place when a person is still a baby. Then the priest dips his thumb in water that has been blessed and traces the Christian cross on the baby's forehead. Then follows the actual baptism in which a little water is poured over the baby's head as a sign of purity and that the baby is now a member of the church.

In other Christian churches, people are baptised when they are old enough to decide for themselves that they want to be baptised. In some churches (especially the Baptist Church), a person is baptised by being 'totally immersed'. That is, the minister lowers them backwards into a pool of water until they are completely immersed for a moment. They are then raised up as a sign that all their sins have been washed away and that they are now beginning a new life.

Water is therefore seen as a way of washing away all that is wrong or unclean; a sign of purity. With its life-giving and refreshing powers, it is also (and perhaps most of all) a symbol of life itself. ◆

96

'ORT'
(Oral Rehydration Therapy)

This short passage shows how much can be done to prevent suffering in the Third World by one extremely simple method. The passage could have a special impact if the assembly leader can mix the life-saving treatment in front of the class. The ingredients required are:

- *4 teaspoons of sugar*
- *1 teaspoon of salt*
- *1 litre of water*

Just how much does it take to save a life? How difficult is it? How easy is it? Take Mali, which is a country in north-west Africa, north of Nigeria, south of Morocco. What could you do to save a dying child in that country?

◆

MALI IS ONE of the five poorest countries in the world and child health care is an urgent priority.

One child in every four dies before reaching its first birthday. And children are so vulnerable to disease and malnutrition that many thousands more do not survive to the age of six. Diarrhoeal disease spread by dirty water is one of the biggest killers of babies and children.

This year, around the world, 3.5 million under-fives could die from severe dehydration caused by diarrhoeal disease. Today alone, 9,600 infants' lives will be lost in the world. That's six for every minute of the day. Yet 4–5 teaspoonfuls of sugar and one teaspoon of salt dissolved in one litre of water is all it would take to save each of those lives.

This sugar-salt mixture can be supplied in sachets containing one complete treatment. Taken by mouth in small regular amounts over a twenty-four hour period, one treatment will completely rehydrate a baby or young child, and replace the vital body salts lost during an attack of diarrhoeal disease.

Each complete treatment costs just 5 pence. The sum of £12 could treat 240 children; £15 could treat 300.

That's 300 lives for 15 quid. ◆

97

Greenpeace

Greenpeace is an international environmental pressure group which maintains complete independence from all political parties anywhere in the world.

You have probably heard of the charity Greenpeace, an organisation that is fighting to improve the environment. But what exactly does Greenpeace stand for?

Greenpeace stands for: a safe and nuclear-free world; fresh air; clean water; the protection of wildlife and natural habitats.

◆

PLANET EARTH is 4,600 million years old. If we condense this incon-ceivable time-span into an understandable concept, we can liken Earth to a person of forty-six years of age. Nothing is known about the first seven years of this person's life, and whilst only scattered information exists about the the middle span, we know that only at the age of forty-two did the Earth begin to flower. Dinosaurs and the great reptiles did not appear until one year ago, when the planet was forty-five. Mammals arrived only eight months ago; in the middle of last week man-like apes evolved into ape-like men, and at the weekend the last Ice Age enveloped the Earth. Modern Man has been around for four hours. During the last hour, Man discovered agriculture. The Industrial Revolution began a minute ago. During those sixty seconds of biological time, Modern Man has made a rubbish tip of Paradise. He has multiplied his numbers to plague proportions, caused the extinction of 500 species of animals, ransacked the planet for fuels and now stands like a brutish infant, gloating over his meteoric rise to ascendancy, on the brink of a ☞

war to end all wars and of effectively destroying this oasis of life in the solar system.

Against all odds

Direct-action campaigns by Greenpeace have alerted the world to major environmental damage. Greenpeace has sailed its ships into nuclear test zones, made itself the target of the whaler's harpoon and thrown itself in the path of chemical dump ships. When these non-violent direct actions were first seen by the world on television screens and in headline newspaper stories, they were greeted with both applause and disbelief. The applause was for the courage of the protesters, the disbelief was that they could take the plight of the natural world so seriously they would risk their lives to save it.

But now the world understands. Humankind has begun to realise its own future is bound up with the survival of the natural world. As a result, governments and industries are obliged to respond. Environmental issues that they would have preferred to keep complicated, and unamendable to public pressure, have been reduced by Greenpeace actions to simple matters of right or wrong. When a Greenpeace volunteer places herself or himself between a hunted whale and the harpoon or between a barrel of toxic waste and the sea, the time for talking is over. It is time to act. Then the public can decide. Against all odds Greenpeace has helped to force the environment on to the political agenda. Now the tide is beginning to turn. Wilderness and wildlife can be preserved, acid rain can be stopped, contamination by chemicals and radioactivity can be brought under control. Peaceful persuasion is proving it can make effective change. ◆

GREENPEACE

98

Hope to Die Before You're Old?

This is a mini-anthology of short readings about old age, designed to help children think about what it means to be old – and perhaps to reconsider the way they regard the old.

Do you like old people? And how are old people treated by other adults younger than them? What sort of happiness or misery must old people feel? And do you dread being really old? So what's it like to be old? Here are a group of short readings about old people. First, Adrian Mole (aged 13 ¾) describes his visit to old-age pensioner Bert Baxter.

◆

BERT BAXTER WAS lying in a filthy-looking bed smoking a cigarette, there was a horrible smell in the room, I think it came from Bert Baxter himself. The bed sheets looked as though they were covered in blood, but Bert said that was caused by the beetroot sandwiches he always ate last thing at night. It was the most disgusting room I have ever seen (and I'm no stranger to squalor). Bert Baxter gave me ten pence and asked me to get him the *Morning Star* from the newsagent's. So he is a communist as well as everything else! Sabre (his Alsatian) usually fetches the paper but he is being kept in as a punishment for chewing the sink.

The man in the newsagent's asked me to give Bert Baxter his bill (he owes for his papers, £31.97), but when I did, Bert Baxter said, 'Smarmy four-eyed git', and laughed and ripped the bill up.

SUE TOWNSEND

But is that how old age should be?

Beautiful Old Age

It ought to be lovely to be old
to be full of the peace that comes of experience
and wrinkled ripe fulfilment.

The wrinkled smile of completeness that follows a life
lived undaunted and unsoured with accepted lies.
If people lived without accepting lies
they would ripen like apples, and be scented like pippins
in their old age.

Soothing, old people should be, like apples
when one is tired of love.
Fragrant like yellowing leaves, and dim with the soft
stillness and satisfaction of autumn.

And a girl should say:
It must be wonderful to live and grow old.
Look at my mother, how rich and still she is! –

And a young man should think: By Jove
my father has faced all weathers, but it's been a life! –

D. H. LAWRENCE

But, of course, old age does mean that our bodies begin to wear out and that we cannot do everything that we used to do. Mind you, there are rewards – as this poem warns us:

Warning

When I am an old woman I shall wear purple
With a red hat which doesn't go, and doesn't suit me,
And I shall spend my pension on brandy and summer gloves
And satin sandals, and say we've no money for butter.
I shall sit down on the pavement when I'm tired
And gobble up samples in shops and press alarm bells
And run my stick along the public railings
And make up for the sobriety of my youth . . .

JENNY JOSEPH

So do you look forward to being old? Will it be good to be old? Here's a very short parable by a Muslim teacher, Idries Shah:

They asked a wise man:

'Which is better, to be young or to be old?'
He said:
'To be old is to have less time before you and more mistakes behind. I leave you to decide whether this is better than the reverse.' ◆

IDRIES SHAH

99

Trinity Hospice

One reason some young people seem to undervalue the gift of life and fail to be aware of the finality of death may be because we have taken so much trouble to shield the young from the reality of death. Elderly relatives are 'put away'. Funerals and cremations are thought to be 'unsuitable' for young children. This passage is included to help pupils to appreciate one aspect of dying – which is still a taboo subject in many circles, but one that will inevitably affect us all. It is about London's oldest hospice for the terminally ill, Trinity.

Some old people are lucky enough to die comfortably at home, with their grown-up children looking after them. Death comes gently and easily as they slip away from this life. Some old people are not so lucky. Their death involves a period of suffering. They are so ill that there is no point in their going into hospital. If the family cannot manage to look after them, they may be sent to a hospice, which is a place where trained staff try to make the dying person's last days as comfortable and as pleasant as possible. This is an account of what it's like in one London hospice called Trinity.

◆

LOTTIE WANTS HER face washed. Never mind that it is spotless, with that shiny honed look of soap and water applied diligently day after day for years. Her hands, thin as paper, flutter.

'Don't fret, darling,' says a young nurse, flannel in hand, as she very tenderly washes and dries the old woman's forehead and mouth.

'Now,' she adds in brisker tones, 'can you eat some more ☞

breakfast – bacon and eggs and another cup of tea?' Lucy swaps a smile, as sweet as the nurse's, and nods.

Ten minutes later she's being fed bacon and eggs and brown toast, gobbling it up with relish. The nurse treats her as gently as she would a new-born baby, even to sighing with satisfaction when the meal is finished.

Later in the morning Bill from the same ward sits in a wheelchair looking out of a window, smoking. 'All he cares about is how many cigs he can get a day. He'll die with a ciggy in his mouth,' says the nurse.

So far Bill hasn't mentioned dying; all he has done since he was admitted two days ago is swear at the nurses and doctors, and hide behind the thinning bones of his face and the thick cough that erupts regularly.

'Men swear, women cry,' comments the ward sister sympathetically and out of earshot. Bill, between eruptions, tells her to bugger off.

Outside the sun is shining after rain. It's a beautiful garden, almost too beautiful with flowing lawns and paths and shrubs, a lake and a wild area sprouting spiky little daffodils in spring. Samuel Pepys lived here in a previous house to escape the smells of London.

It's almost the same today, but now the inhabitants are advanced cancer patients.

Bill has a brand-new wireless and earphones by his side, a bunch of grapes, *The Sun* newspaper. He puffs, coughs, puffs again.

The ward's day room is furnished in that uncoordinated way common to such places; an upright piano, a television, music cassettes, an eclectic selection of books that has James Hadley Chase's *Hand Me a Fig Leaf* nestling against *Village Affairs* by ☞

Miss Read. Two budgies in a cage talk and twitter dementedly until a fed-up someone plonks a cover over their cage.

Two shiny black cats contentedly walk the downstairs ward. They're known as Dex and Morph – after Dexonethesone and morphine – the hospice is not without a welcome gallows humour on occasions.

This bright day the cats take their ease on an empty bed that catches the sun. They are watched by a patient, totally silent and motionless, whose last energy seems to reside in his eyes.

There is an odd bleakness by his bed that nags: yes, of course, what troubles is that there are no books or cards or bottles of squash, least of all family photographs, by his side. There is none of the personal clutter and paraphernalia that establish identity against the white tidiness of the hospice bed.

'You'd be amazed at how many have no family or relatives, or severed connections too long ago,' says the ward sister, a woman of much kindness and unusual observation.

Say this to her and she will maintain that observation and intuition are an important part of the job – particularly when her patients are too old and tired and ill to talk much. Or too frightened. Or too reluctant. It's called the British way of death. It doesn't happen much at Trinity because that's what they're trying to avoid.

In the next bay two old ladies are dying in diametrically opposed ways. One is slipping down the gentle slope of her final days tranquilly, her quiet breath hardly disturbing the sunlit dust motes above her bed. The other, Scottish with an Edinburgh accent, propped up on pillows, skeletal from the wasting disease that has triumphed, is cross that she is still alive.

'Why didn't I die last night?' she demands angrily. 'Why can't I die in my sleep?'

'She's not afraid of dying,' says a nurse, 'only of how she dies.'

'People die as they live. We had a tough lorry driver in here last year. Nothing would get him into a bed to die, he swore, and nothing did. He died suddenly in a reclining chair with a cigarette still in his mouth.

'We never introduce the word death to them but let them come to us, in a manner of speaking. They set the pace. We don't intrude, just encourage . . . '

'Hospice nursing is real nursing,' said another. 'I'd done every sort of nursing before I came here but this is the real thing.

'They can still enjoy things. Last year we took one old lady to Wimbledon just before she died. She'd always wanted to go. She loved it.'

'It's made me less afraid of my own death,' said a voluntary worker.

'It's total care – care of the body, mind and spirit,' added a colleague. 'We can only take advanced cancer patients at Trinity because that's our area but I believe all terminally ill people need this type of support.'

A wife sits by her dying husband. He is asleep, breathing noisily, his face almost resting on her comfortable breast. She is glad that he is in here.

'I had my first proper sleep last night for weeks. I felt he was being properly looked after. I could sit here all day, there isn't much time left. He won't talk about it but I think he's at peace with himself.

'Look,' she lifts up a sort of bedcover she's crocheting. 'I'll make ☛

one for them here to remember him by.'

Outside there is the rattle of the dinner trolley. Sister shouts: 'Anyone for sherry?' The wife of the dying man accepts a glass of sweet sherry and sips it nervously. It's not something she associates with hospitals but then this isn't a hospital: it's a hospice. ◆

KATE WHARTON

100

What's It Like to Die?

If we were able to answer this question, we would presumably live our lives very differently. Christians believe that Jesus came back from the dead to show us there is life after death. Otherwise there is no firm evidence of what lies in wait for us after death. This article appeared in the Observer Magazine *in 1990. In it, Simon Hoggart reports on a conference of European sceptics, and in particular on a paper delivered by a psychologist, Dr Susan Blackmore, in which she talked about 'near-death experiences'.*

I wonder if you have ever thought what it's like to die? Not horribly and suddenly in, say, a road accident, but when you are conscious, perhaps in a hospital bed or at home? Some people have had 'near-death experiences': that is, when they have been very close to dying, but when doctors have been able to bring them back to life. This is a newspaper article that reports on what experiences such people felt as they approached death. Later in the article the reporter describes what one psychologist has discovered. A psychologist is a person who studies the mind and how it works.

————————————— ◆ —————————————

IT'S ASTONISHING HOW much people's experiences have in common. Most report a tremendous feeling of 'peace' as death approaches. Many (about 37 per cent, according to one survey) feel they separate from their own body. Some sense they are looking down on themselves, and can see, for example, the wreckage of the car and the ambulancemen.

A large number of such people have the sensation of going into a tunnel. At the end is a bright light, which grows bigger. As ☞

many as 10 per cent enter this light, where they encounter a wonderful world, with friends and relatives who have already died welcoming them.

There are other curiosities. Many feel that they have a choice, to live or die. Some decided to return to life for a good reason, such as caring for their children. Others gave more banal excuses; one woman said she had to do the ironing. This suggests that the 'choice' may just be a rationalisation.

Hindus in India often report that they felt they were being called by the devil, but are told that there's been a mistake, so they can return.

Another strange thing is that many people who have been near death return as nicer human beings. There are cases of yuppies selling the Porsche, quitting the rat race and becoming charity workers. Most near-death survivors say they now face the thought of death with great equanimity and even pleasure.

Thousands of people report these experiences, so it's clearly not simply nonsense. But what is it? A Christian could argue that the experience is real; the people who 'enter the light' are indeed in heaven. Children who just survived the many diseases of the last century often told of meeting others who had died before them. But modern children have described being met by schoolfriends who are still alive.

One psychologist has worked on several theories. The tunnel may be the result of oxygen starvation which suppresses inhibitors and makes cells fire in the visual cortex. The sense of looking down on oneself may be the brain trying to create a model from such sensory input as it can get: noise, pain, touch and so forth.

It is true that people do see their past life flashing in front of ☞

them, but usually in the form of a muddled batch of memories rather than a chronological history. Nobody is sure why.

And why are so many people changed in the life they have spared? The psychologist Dr Blackmore suggests that, from birth, we construct a model of ourselves in our own minds, a 'self' which we create and then cling on to. Shake that loose and we become, literally as well as figuratively, less self-centred.

What is most heartening, though, is that the experience of dying seems so very pleasant for so many people. What we can never know is what it's like for people who die instantaneously. But then having your head chopped off never was much fun. ◆

SIMON HOGGART

Calendar

Charities

whose work is described in this anthology

Action Aid
Tapstone Road
Chard
Somerset
TA20 2AB

Care
36 Southampton St
London
SW2E 7HE

Centrepoint Soho
5th Floor
140A Gloucester Mansions
Cambridge Circus
London
WC2H 8HD

Christian Aid
PO Box 1
London
SW9 8BN

Greenpeace
30–31 Islington Green
London
N1 8XE

The Leprosy Mission
England and Wales
Goldhay Way
Orton Goldhay
Peterborough
PE2 0GZ